P9-EMD-902

THE TRAIL OF THE SANDHILL STAG

AND OTHER LIVES OF THE HUNTED

THE TRAIL OF THE SANDHILL STAG

and other Lives of the Hunted

by Ernest Thompson Seton

Illustrated with a colour frontispiece by
RITA PARSONS
and line drawings in the text by
the author

LONDON: J. M. DENT & SONS LTD
NEW YORK: E. P. DUTTON & CO. INC.

ERNEST THOMPSON SETON was born on 14th August 1860 at South Shields, Durham, one of a family of fourteen. When he was six they emigrated to Canada, first to Lindsay, Ontario, and then settling in Toronto. Returning to Lindsay for a summer in 1875 gave him the setting and many of the adventures for his greatest book, 'Two Little Savages' (1903), and from thenceforward Seton devoted himself to nature study. Later he became Naturalist to the Government of Manitoba and author of the standard work 'Life Histories of Northern Animals' (1909). Besides this he was founder of the Woodcraft Movement which was soon amalgamated with the Scout Movement, and he became Chief Scout of America.

As early as 1884 Seton began contributing short accounts of the true adventures of actual animals to various magazines, and his authentic account of how he trapped Lobo the great wolf of Currumpaw appeared in 'Scribner's' in 1894. In 1898 he collected the best of these animal biographies as 'Wild Animals I Have Known', which became a best-seller immediately and brought him world-wide renown. He followed it with many excellent stories, long or short, of animal heroes, the most notable being 'The Trail of the Sandhill Stag' (1899), 'Lives of the Hunted' (1901), 'Monarch, The Big Bear' (1904) and 'Bannertail: the Story of a Grey Squirrel' (1922).

Besides 'Two Little Savages' (1903) Seton wrote another tale of backwoods adventure, 'Rolf in the Woods' (1911); and his admirable autobiography, 'Trail of an Artist-Naturalist' (1951) was published some years after his death in 1946.

 Made in Great Britain at the Aldine Press, Letchworth, Herts, for J. M. Dent & Sons Ltd, Aldine House, Bedford Street, London. First published in this edition 1966.

To the
PRESERVATION OF OUR WILD CREATURES
I dedicate this book

E.T.S. 

INTRODUCTION

THERE have been stories whose heroes were animals ever since stories were told. The fairy-tales are full of them, and long before Puss in Boots the ancient Greeks were telling of the friendly beasts and birds who helped Melampus the seer, who could understand their language, to win his princess.

Much nearer our own time we find cats and caterpillars, hares and rabbits talking their delightfully logical nonsense in Wonderland, and can read *The Autobiography of a Horse* (better known as *Black Beauty*).

While the White Rabbit and the March Hare belong, like the Snark and the Bandersnatch, to a world of their own, Anna Sewell's hero is a real horse living the typical life of an English horse a hundred years ago. Beauty tells his own story, however, and he and his friends talk to one another and understand the words of the men for whom they work.

The same is true of the animals in Kipling's *Jungle Books*, even if Mowgli has to learn both their language and that of the Man Pack. Baloo and Bagheera are true bear and panther, and Kaa is a genuine python—but they are something more: 'Since Kipling had no knowledge of natural history, and makes no effort to present it, and since furthermore his animals talk and live like men, his stories are not animal stories in the realistic sense; they are wonderful, beautiful fairy-tales.' So Ernest Thompson Seton described them, and of all writers he was best qualified to make distinctions between realism and romance in stories of animals.

For, wrote the naturalist Clarence Hawkes, it was 'Ernest Thompson Seton who blazed the trail for the new school of American nature writers, and whose classical animal stories have caused tens of thousands of people, who never cared for nature before, to become interested in out-of-door life'.

The eleventh of fourteen children, Ernest Thompson Seton was born on 14th August 1860 at South Shields, and his family emigrated to Canada when he was six, settling in Toronto after a short period at Lindsay, Ontario. From the start he showed an instinctive interest in natural history, both observing and drawing the wild life which was all about him, or within easy reach. He received little encouragement from his family, but ill health when he was about fifteen led them to send him for the summer months to lodge with a farmer called William Blackwell, who had bought their old farm at Lindsay.

Very soon Ernest and Blackwell's son George were camping out in the woods, striving to live as the Red Indians had done before the coming of the Paleface. 'It was at Blackwell's that I built the dam and led the other boys in the ways of Indian life,' he wrote in his autobiography nearly seventy years later. 'It was there that I built my first tepee, and made bows and arrows, and did all I could to re-establish Indian ways. . . . It was there that I met Caleb Clark, and from him learnt much of woods and wild life. It was there that I renewed the acquaintance of the Sanger Witch, and from her gathered a very wealth of woodlore. . . . Each summer came with renewed promise of this visit to my Eden-land.'

Readers of *Two Little Savages* (1903) have never been in any doubt as to the truth of that delightful narrative—the only ancestor, except for *Bevis*, of those supreme chronicles of holiday adventures, *Swallows and Amazons* and its sequels: *The Trail of an Artist-Naturalist* does no more than underline a few of the incidents.

His summers at 'Sanger' turned Ernest Thompson Seton's interests and energies definitely towards nature study. But on leaving school he spent several years studying art at Toronto and in London.

After that there were years of struggle toward the

achievement of his ambition. But during these years he was collecting knowledge and experiences which he was to use later—first of all in stories and sketches in magazines, and then in the books which he made out of them. There was Lobo, the great wolf of Currumpaw whom he trapped in 1894; the adventures of his own dog Bingo, and of the 'yaller dog' Wully, and many more.

When at last he collected these into a book called *Wild Animals I have Known* in 1898, it became suddenly a best seller and he a famous author whose work was known and read all over the world. He followed it with his most famous book *The Trail of the Sandhill Stag* (1899), with more collections of shorter tales about animals he had known, such as *Lives of the Hunted* (1901), and other biographies such as that of *Monarch the Big Bear* (1904) and *Bannertail: The Story of a Grey Squirrel* (1922). He turned back to his own boyhood in *Two Little Savages*, and tried his hand less successfully at an adventure story of a boy's experiences in Canada a hundred years earlier, *Rolf in the Woods* (1911).

Besides writing about boys' adventures 'in the woods', Seton founded the Woodcraft Indians with town boys camping in tribes as amateur Indians, like Sam and Yan in *Two Little Savages*. Later this became a part of the Boy Scout movement, and Seton was elected the Chief Scout of America.

But above all he was known and loved for his stories of animals: the new sort of story which he invented, and which he described as the 'giving in fiction form the actual facts of an animal's life and modes of thought'. Of these 'zoographies' he wrote: 'When I look at the names of the animals whose stories I have given here, I feel much as an artist might in looking at sundry portraits of his friends and ideals painted by himself. Some of these I personally knew. Some are composites, and are merely natural history in story form.'

It is this combination of authentic natural history cast into thrilling story form, with first-class illustrations thrown in for good measure, that gives Ernest Thompson Seton his unique place. He has had many followers and imitators, some as good and memorable as Charles G. D. Roberts and Henry Williamson: but his are the stories we remember best, and the animals whom he describes remain in our memories more vividly even than Red Fox or Tarka the Otter. Those of us who are lucky enough to find the stories when we are young can never forget the thrill of meeting Lobo or Tito or Johnny Bear, Krag the Kootenay Ram or Bannertail the Squirrel, Raggylug the Rabbit, Warb the Grizzly and Monarch the Big Bear of Tallac—even Way-Atcha the Coon-Raccoon of Kilder Creek and Redruff the Don Valley Partridge, to say nothing of a host of dogs, Bingo, Wully, Chink, Billy and the rest.

In their own way they can come to hold a place in our affections almost as high as that held by Bagheera and Baloo and Akela: they may not be such close friends, but they are acquaintances in whom we take a vital interest, grieving over their sorrows and joying in their triumphs. And never again after reading these stories can we look at the wild life about us with quite the same eyes: we may not be able to speak the language of the beasts, but Ernest Thompson Seton is surely the best interpreter they have ever had.

ROGER LANCELYN GREEN.

1966.

CONTENTS

The Trail of the Sandhill Stag

I

IT WAS a burning hot day. Yan was wandering in pursuit of birds among the endless groves and glades of the Sandhill wilderness about Carberry. The water in the numerous marshy ponds was warm with the sun heat, so Yan cut across to the trail spring, the only place in the country where he might find a cooling drink. As he stooped beside it his eye fell on a small hoof-mark in the mud, a sharp and elegant track. He had never seen one like it before, but it gave him a thrill, for he knew at once it was the track of a *wild deer*.

'There are no deer in those hills now,' the settlers told Yan. Yet when the first snow came that autumn he, remembering the hoof-mark in the mud, quietly took down his rifle and said to himself, 'I am going into the hills every day till I bring out a deer.' Yan was a tall, raw lad in the last of his teens. He was no hunter yet, but he was a tireless runner, and filled with unflagging zeal. Away to the hills he went on his quest day after day, and many a score of long white miles he coursed, and night after night he returned to the shanty without seeing even a track. But the longest chase will end. On a far, hard trip in the southern hills he came at last on the trail of a deer—dim and stale, but still a deer-trail—and again he felt a thrill as the thought came, 'At the other end of that line of dimples in the snow is the creature that made them; each one is fresher than the last, and it is only a question of time for me to come up with their maker.'

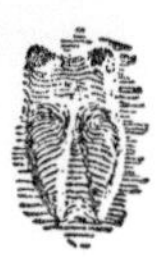

At first Yan could not tell by the dim track which way the animal had gone. But he soon found that the mark was a little sharper at one end, and rightly guessed that that was the toe; also he noticed that the spaces shortened in going uphill, and at last a clear imprint in a sandy place ended all doubt. Away he went with a new fire in his blood, and an odd prickling in his hair; away on a long, hard follow through interminable woods and hills, with the trail growing fresher as he flew. All day he followed, and toward night it turned and led him homeward. On it went, soon over familiar ground, back to the sawmill, then over Mitchell's Plain, and at last into the thick poplar woods near by, where Yan left it when it was too dark to follow. He was only seven miles from home, and this he easily trotted in an hour.

In the morning he was back to take it up, but, instead of an old track, there were now so many fresh ones, crossing and winding, that he could not follow at all. So he prowled along haphazard, until he found two tracks so new that he could easily trail them as before, and he eagerly gave chase. As he sneaked along watching the tracks at his feet instead of the woods ahead, he was startled by two big-eared, greyish animals springing from a little glade into which he had stumbled. They trotted to a bank fifty yards away and then turned to gaze at him.

How they did seem to *look* with their great ears! How they spellbound him by the soft gaze that he felt rather than saw! He knew what they were. Had he not for weeks been holding ready, preparing and hungering for this very sight! And yet how useless were his preparations; how wholly all his preconcepts were swept away, and a wonder-stricken 'Oh-h-h!' went softly from his throat.

As he stood and gazed, they turned their heads away, though they still seemed to look at him with their great ears and, trotting a few steps to a smoother place, began to bound up and down in a sort of play. They seemed to have forgotten him, and it was bewildering to see the wonderful effortless way in which, by a tiny toe-touch, they would rise

six or eight feet in air. Yan stood fascinated by the strange play of the light-limbed, grey-furred creatures. There was no haste or alarm in their movements; he would watch them until they began to run away—till they should take fright and begin the laboured straining, the vast athletic bounds, he had heard of. And it was only on noting that they were rapidly fading into the distance that he realized that *now* they were running away, *already* were flying for safety.

Higher and higher they rose each time; gracefully their bodies swayed inward as they curved along some bold ridge, or for a long space the buff-white scutcheons that they bore behind them seemed hanging in the air while these wingless birds were really sailing over some deep gully.

Yan stood intensely gazing until they were out of sight, and it never once occurred to him to shoot.

When they were gone he went to the place where they had begun their play. Here was one track; where was the next? He looked all around and was surprised to see a blank for fifteen feet; and then another blank, and on farther, another; then the blanks increased to eighteen feet, then to twenty, then to twenty-five and sometimes thirty feet. Each of these playful, effortless bounds covered a space of eighteen to thirty feet.

Gods above! They do not run at all—they fly; and once in a while come down again to tap the hill-tops with their dainty hoofs.

'I'm glad they got away,' said Yan. 'They've shown me something today that never man saw before. I know that no one else has ever seen it, or he would have told of it.'

II

YET when the morning came the old wolfish instinct was back in his heart. 'I must away to the hills,' he said, 'take up the trail, and be a beast of the chase once more; my wits against their wits; my strength against their strength; and against their speed, my gun.'

Oh, those glorious hills—an endless rolling stretch of sandy dunes, with lakes and woods and grassy lawns between! Life—life on every side, and life within, for Yan

was young and strong and joyed in powers complete. 'These are the best days of my life,' he said, 'these are my golden days.' He thought it then, and oh, how well he came to know it in the after years!

All day at a long wolf-lope he would go and send the white hare and the partridge flying from his path, and swing along and scan the ground for sign and the telltale inscript in the snow, the oldest of all writing, more thrillful of interest by far than the finest glyph or scarab that ever Egypt gave to modern day.

But the driving snow was the wild deer's friend, as the driven snow was his foe, and down it came that day and wiped out every trace.

The next day and the next still found Yan careering in the hills, but never a track or sign did he see. And the weeks went by, and many a rolling mile he ran, and many a bitter day and freezing night he passed in the snow-clad hills,

sometimes on a deer-trail but more often without; sometimes in the barren hills, and sometimes led by woodmen's talk to far-off sheltering woods, and once or twice he saw indeed the buff-white bannerets go floating up the hills. Sometimes reports came of a great buck that frequented the timber-lands near the sawmill, and more than once Yan found his trail, but never got a glimpse of him; and the few deer there were now grew so wild with long pursuit that he had no further chances to shoot, and the hunting season passed in one long train of failures.

Bright, unsad failures they. He seemed indeed to come back empty-handed, but he really came home laden with the best spoils of the chase, and he knew it more and more, as time went on, till every day, at last, on the clear unending trail, was a glad triumphant march.

III

THE years went by. Another season came, and Yan felt in his heart the hunter fret once more. Even had he not, the talk he heard would have set him all afire.

It told of a mighty buck that now lived in the hills—the Sandhill Stag, they called him. It told of his size, his speed and the crowning glory that he bore on his brow, a marvellous growth like sculptured bronze with gleaming ivory points.

So, when the first tracking snow came, Yan set out with some comrades who had caught a faint reflected glow of his ardour. They drove in a sleigh to the Spruce Hill, then scattered to meet again at sunset. The woods about abounded in hares and grouse, and the powder burned all around. But no deer-track was to be found, so Yan quietly left the woods

and set off alone for Kennedy's Plain, where last this wonderful buck had been seen.

After a few miles he came on a great deer-track, so large and sharp and broken by such mighty bounds that he knew it at once for the trail of the Sandhill Stag.

With a sudden rush of strength to his limbs he led away like a wolf on the trail. And down his spine and in his hair he felt as before, and yet as never before, the strange prickling that he knew was the same as makes the wolf's mane bristle when he hunts. He followed till night was near and he must needs turn, for the Spruce Hill was many miles away.

He knew that it would be long after sunset before he could get there, and he scarcely expected that his comrades would wait for him, but he did not care; he gloried in the independence of his strength, for his legs were like iron and his wind was like a hound's. Ten miles were no more to him than a mile to another man, for he could run all day and come home fresh, and always when alone in the lone hills he felt within so glad a gush of wild exhilaration that his joy was full.

So when his friends, feeling sure that he could take care of himself, drove home and left him, he was glad to be left. They seemed rather to pity him for imposing on himself such long toilsome tramps. They had no realization of what he found in those wind-swept hills. They never once thought what they and all their friends and every man that ever lived has striven for and offered his body, his brain, his freedom and his life to buy; what they were vainly wearing out their lives in fearful, hopeless drudgery to gain, that boy was daily finding in those hills. The bitter, biting, blizzard wind was without, but the fire of health and youth was within; and at every stride in his daily march, it was *happiness* he found, and he knew it. And he smiled such a gentle smile when he thought of those driven home in the sleigh shivering and miserable, *yet pitying him.*

Oh, what a glorious sunset he saw that day on Kennedy's

Plain, with the snow dyed red and the poplar woods aglow in pink and gold! What a glorious tramp through the darkening woods as the shadows fell and the yellow moon came up!

'These are the best days of my life,' he sang. 'These are my golden days!'

And as he neared the great Spruce Hill, Yan yelled a long hurrah! 'In case they are still there,' he told himself, but really for very joy of feeling all alive.

As he listened for the improbable response, he heard a faint howling of wolves away over Kennedy's Plain. He mimicked their cry and quickly got response, and noticed that they were gathering together, doubtless hunting something, for now it was their hunting-cry. Nearer and nearer it came, and his howls brought ready answers from the gloomy echoing woods, when suddenly it flashed upon him: 'It's *my* trail you are on. *You are hunting me.*'

The road now led across a little open plain. It would have been madness to climb a tree in such a fearful frost, so he went out to the middle of the open place and sat down in the moonlit snow—a glittering rifle in his hands, a row of shining brass pegs in his belt and a strange new feeling in his heart. On came the chorus, a deep melodious howling, on to the very edge of the woods, and there the note changed. Then there was silence. They must have seen him sitting there, for the light was like day, but they went around in the edge of the woods. A stick snapped to the right and a low '*Woof*' came from the left. Then all was still. Yan felt them sneaking around, felt them watching him from the cover and strained his eyes in vain to see some form that he might shoot. But they were wise, and he was wise, for had he run he would soon have seen them closing in on him. They must have been but few, for after their council of war they decided he was better let alone, and he never saw them at all. For twenty minutes he waited, but, hearing no more of them, arose and went homeward. And as he tramped he thought, 'Now I know how a deer feels

when the grind of a moccasined foot or the click of a lock is heard in the trail behind him.'

In the days that followed he learned those Sandhills well, for many a frosty day and bitter night he spent in them. He learned to follow fast the faintest trail of deer. He learned just why that trail went never past a tamarack tree, and why it pawed the snow at every oak, and why the buck's is plainest and the fawn's down-wind. He learned just what the club-rush has to say when its tussocks break the snow. He came to know how the musk-rat lives beneath the ice, and why the mink slides down a hill, and what the ice says when it screams at night. The squirrels taught him how best a fir cone can be stripped and which of toadstools one might eat; the partridge, why it dives beneath the snow, and the fox, just why he sets his feet so straight, and why he wears so huge a tail.

He learned the ponds, the woods, the hills and a hundred secrets of the trail, but—*he got no deer*.

And though many a score of crooked frosty miles he coursed, and sometimes had a track to lead and sometimes none, he still went on, like Galahad when the Grail was just before him. For more than once, the guide that led was the trail of the Sandhill Stag.

IV

THE hunt was nearly over, for the season's end was nigh. The moose-birds had picked the last of the saskatoons, all the spruce cones were scaled and the hunger-moon was at hand. But a hopeful chickadee sang '*See soon*' as Yan set off one frosty day for the great Spruce Woods. On the road he overtook a woodcutter, who told him that at such a place he had seen two deer last night—a doe and a monstrous stag with 'a rocking-chair on his head'.

Straight to the very place went Yan, and found the

tracks—one like those he had seen in the mud long ago, another a large unmistakable print, the mark of the Sandhill Stag.

How the wild beast in his heart did ramp—he wanted to howl like a wolf on a hot scent; and away they went through woods and hills, the trail and Yan and the inner wolf.

All day he followed and, grown crafty himself, remarked each sign, and rejoiced to find that nowhere had the deer been bounding. And when the sun was low the sign was warm, so, laying aside unneeded things, Yan crawled along like a snake on the track of a hare. All day the animals had zigzagged as they fed; their drink was snow, and now at length away across a lawn in a bank of brush Yan spied a *something* flash. A bird perhaps; he lay still and watched. Then, grey among the grey brush, he made out a great log, and from one end of it rose two gnarled oaken boughs. Again the flash—the move of a restless ear, then the oak boughs moved and Yan trembled, for he knew that the log in the brush was the form of the Sandhill Stag. So grand, so charged with *life*. He seemed a precious, sacred thing—a king, fur-robed and duly crowned. To think of shooting now as he lay unconscious, resting, seemed an awful crime. But Yan for weeks and months had pined for this. His chance had come, and shoot he must. The long, long strain grew tighter yet—grew taut—broke down, as up the rifle went. But the wretched thing kept wobbling and pointing all about the little glade. His breath came hot and fast and choking—so much, so very much, so clearly all, hung on a single touch. He laid the rifle down, revulsed—and trembled in the snow. But he soon regained the mastery, his hand was steady now, the sights in line—'twas but a deer out yonder. But at that moment the Stag turned full Yan's way, with those regardful eyes and ears, and nostrils too, and gazed.

'Darest thou slay me?' said an uncrowned, unarmed king once, as his eyes fell on the assassin's knife, and in that clear, calm gaze the murderer quailed and cowed.

So trembled Yan; but he knew it was only stag-fever, and he despised it then as he came in time to honour it; and the beast that dwelt within him fired the gun.

The ball splashed short. The buck sprang up and the doe appeared. Another shot; then, as they fled, another and another. But away the deer went, lightly drifting across the low round hills.

V

He followed their trail for some time, but gnashed his teeth to find no sign of blood, and he burned with a raging animal sense that was neither love nor hate. Within a mile there was a new sign that joined on and filled him with another rage and shed light on many a bloody page of frontier history—a moccasin track, a straight-set, broad-toed, moosehide track, the track of a Cree brave. He followed in savage humour, and as he careered up a slope a tall form rose from a log, raising one hand in peaceable gesture. Although Yan was behind, the Indian had seen him first.

'Who are you?' said Yan roughly.

'Chaska.'

'What are you doing in my country?'

'It was my country first,' he replied gravely.

'Those are my deer,' Yan said, and thought.

'No man owns wild deer till he kills them,' said Chaska.

'You better keep off any trail I'm following.'

'Not afraid,' said he, and made a gesture to include the whole settlement, then added gently, 'No good to fight; the best man will get the most deer anyhow.'

And the end of it was that Yan stayed for several days with Chaska, and got, not an antlered buck indeed, but, better far, an insight into the ways of a man who could hunt. The Indian taught him *not* to follow the trail over the hills, for deer watch their back track, and cross the hills to make

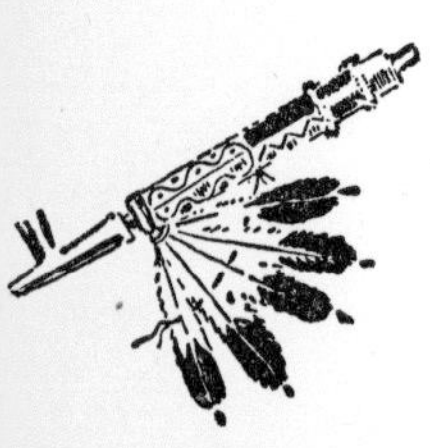

this more easy. He taught him to tell by touch and smell of sign just how far ahead they are, as well as the size and condition of the deer, and not to trail closely when the game is near. He taught him to study the wind by raising his moistened finger in the air, and Yan thought, 'Now I know why a deer's nose is always moist, for he must always watch the wind.' He showed Yan how much may be gained at times by patient waiting, and that it is better to tread like an Indian with foot set straight, for thereby one gains an inch or two at each stride and can come back in one's own track through deep snow. And he also unwittingly taught him that an Indian *cannot* shoot with a rifle, and Natty Bumpo's adage came to mind: 'A white man can shoot with a gun, but it ain't accordin' to an Injun's gifts.'

Sometimes they went out together and sometimes singly. One day, while out alone, Yan had followed a deer-track into a thicket by what is now called Chaska Lake. The sign was fresh, and as he sneaked around there was a rustle in the brush. Then he saw the kinnikinnick boughs shaking. His gun flew up and covered the spot. As soon as he was sure of the place he meant to fire. But when he saw the creature as a dusky moving form through the twigs, he awaited a better view, which came, and he had almost pulled the trigger when his hand was stayed by a glimpse of red, and a moment later out stepped—Chaska.

'Chaska,' Yan gasped, 'I nearly did for you!'

For reply the Indian drew his finger across the red handkerchief on his brow. Yan knew then one reason why a hunting Indian always wears it; after that he wore one himself.

One day a flock of prairie chickens flew high overhead toward the thick spruce woods. Others followed, and it seemed to be a general move. Chaska looked toward them and said, 'Chickens go hide in bush. Blizzard tonight.'

It surely came, and the hunters stayed all day by the fire. Next day it was as fierce as ever. On the third day it ceased somewhat, and they hunted again. But Chaska returned with his gun broken by a fall, and after a long silent smoke he said:

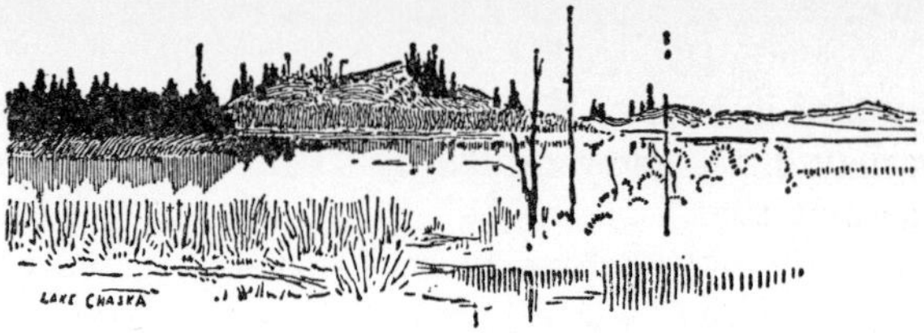

'Yan hunt in Moose Mountain?'

'No!'

'Good hunting. Go?'

Yan shook his head.

Presently the Indian, glancing to the eastward, said, 'Sioux tracks there today. All bad medicine here.' And Yan knew that his mind was made up. He went away and they never met again, and all that is left of him now is his name, borne by the lonely lake that lies in the Carberry Hills.

VI

'THERE are more deer round Carberry now than ever before, and the Big Stag has been seen between Kennedy's Plain and the mill.' So said a note that reached Yan away in the east, where he had been chafing in a new and distasteful life. It was the beginning of the hunting season, the fret was already in his blood, and that letter decided him. For a while the iron horse, for a while the gentle horse, then he donned his moosehide wings and flew as of old on many a long hard flight, to return as so often before.

Then he heard that at a certain lake far to the eastward seven deer had been seen: their leader a wonderful buck.

With three others he set out in a sleigh to the eastward lake, and soon found the tracks—six of various sizes and one large one, undoubtedly that of the famous Stag.

How utterly the veneer was torn to tatters by those seven chains of tracks! How completely the wild palaeolithic beast stood revealed in each of the men, in spite of semi-modern garb, as they drove away on the trail with a wild, excited gleam in every eye!

It was nearly night before the trail warmed up, but even then, in spite of Yan's earnest protest, they drove on in the sleigh. And soon they came to where the trail told of seven keen observers looking backward from a hill, then an even sevenfold chain of twenty-five foot bounds. The hunters got no glimpse at all, but followed till the night came down, then hastily camped in the snow.

In the morning they followed as before, and soon came to where seven spots of black, bare ground showed where the deer had slept.

Now when the trail grew warm Yan insisted on hunting on foot. He trailed the deer into a great thicket, and knew just where they were by a grouse that flew cackling from its farther side.

He arranged a plan, but his friends would not await the blue-jay's 'all right' note, and the deer escaped. But finding themselves hard pressed, they split their band, two going one way and five another. Yan kept with him one, Duff, and leaving the others to follow the five deer, he took up the twofold trail. Why? Because in it was the great broad track he had followed for two years back.

On they went, overtaking the deer and causing them again to split. Yan sent Duff after the doe, while he stuck relentlessly to the track of the famous Stag. As the sun got low the chase led to a great half-wooded stretch, in a country new to him; for he had driven the Stag far from his ancient range. The trail again grew hot, but just as Yan felt sure he soon would close, two distant shots were heard, and the track of the Stag as he found it then went off in a fear-winged flight that might keep on for miles.

Yan went at a run, and soon found Duff. He had had two long shots at the doe. The second he thought had hit her. Within half a mile they found blood on the trail; within another half-mile the blood was no more seen and the track

seemed to have grown very large and strong. The snow was drifting and the marks not easily read, yet Yan knew very soon that the track they were on was not that of the wounded doe, but was surely that of her antlered mate. Back on the trail they ran till they solved the doubt, for there they learned that the Stag, after making his own escape, had come back to change off: an old, old trick of the hunted whereby one deer will cleverly join on and carry on the line of tracks to save another that is too hard pressed, while it leaps aside to hide or fly in a different direction. Thus the Stag had sought to save his wounded mate, but the hunters remorselessly took up her trail and gloated like wolves over the slight drip of blood. Within another short run they found that the Stag, having failed to divert the chase to himself, had returned to her, and at sundown they sighted them a quarter of a mile ahead mounting a long snow slope. The doe was walking slowly, with hanging head and ears. The buck was running about as though in trouble that he did not understand, and coming back to caress the doe and wonder why she walked so slowly. In another half-mile the hunters came up with them. She was down in the snow. When he saw them coming, the great Stag shook the oak tree on his brow and circled about in doubt, then fled from a foe he was powerless to resist.

As the men came near the doe made a convulsive effort to rise, but could not. Duff drew his knife. It never before occurred to Yan why he and each of them carried a long knife. The poor doe turned on her foes her great lustrous eyes; they were brimming with tears, but she made no moan. Yan turned his back on the scene and covered his face with his hands, but Duff went forward with the knife and did some dreadful, unspeakable thing, Yan scarcely knew what, and when Duff called him he slowly turned, and the big Stag's mate was lying quiet in the snow, and the only living thing that they saw as they quit the scene was the great round form bearing aloft the oak tree on its brow as it haunted the nearer hills.

And when, an hour later, the men came with the sleigh to lift the doe's body from the crimsoned snow, there were large fresh tracks about it, and a dark shadow passed over the whitened hill into the silent night.

What morbid thoughts came from the fire that night! How the man in Yan did taunt the glutted brute! Was this the end? Was this the real chase? After long weeks, with the ideal alone in mind, after countless blessed failures, was this the vile success—a beautiful, glorious, living creature tortured into a loathsome mass of carrion?

VII

BUT when the morning came the impress of the night was dim. A long howl came over the hill, and the thought that a wolf was on the trail that he was quitting smote sadly on Yan's heart. They all set out for the settlement, but within an hour Yan only wanted an excuse to stay. And when at length they ran on to the fresh track of the Sandhill Stag himself, the lad was all ablaze once more.

'I cannot go back—something tells me that I must stay—I must see him face to face again.'

The rest had had enough of the bitter frost, so Yan took from the sleigh a small pot, a blanket and some food, and left them, to follow alone the great sharp imprint in the snow.

'Goodbye—good luck!'

He watched the sleigh out of sight, in the low hills, and then felt as he never had before. Though he had been so many months alone in the wilds, he had never known loneliness, but as soon as his friends were gone he was overwhelmed by a sense of the utter heart-sickening dreariness of the endless snowy waste. Where were the charms that he had never failed to find until now? He wanted to recall the sleigh, but pride kept him silent.

In a little while it was too late, and soon he was once more in the power of that fascinating, endless chain of tracks—a chain begun years ago, when in a June the track of a mother Blacktail was suddenly joined by two little ones' tracks. Since then the three had gone on winding over the land the trail-chains they were forging—knotted and kinked and twisted with every move and thought of the makers, imprinted with every hap of their lives, but interrupted never wholly. At times the tracks were joined by that of some fierce foe, and the kind of mark was changed, but the chains went on for months and years, now fast, now slow, but endless, until some foe more strong joined on and there one trail was ended. But this great Stag was forging still that mystic chain. A million roods of hills had he overlaid with its links, had scribbled over in this oldest script with the story of his life. If only our eyes were bright enough to follow up that twenty thousand miles of trail, what light unguessed we might obtain where the wisest now are groping!

But, skin deep, man is brute. Just a little while ago we were mere hunting brutes—our bellies were our only thought, that telltale line of dots was the road to food. No man can follow it far without feeling a wild beast prickling in his hair and down his spine. Away Yan went, a hunter-brute once more, all other feelings swamped.

Late that day the trail, after many a kink and seeming break, led into a great dense thicket of brittle, quaking asp. Yan knew that the Stag was there to lie at rest. The deer went in up-wind, of course. His eyes and ears would watch his trail, and his nose would guard in front, so Yan went in at one side, trusting to get a shot. With a very agony of care he made his way, step by step, and, after many minutes, surely found the track, still leading on. Another lengthy crawl, with nerves at tense, and then the lad thought he heard a twig snapped behind him, though the track was still ahead. And after long he found it true. Before lying down the Stag had doubled back, and while Yan had thought him still ahead, he was lying far behind, so had got wind of the man and now was miles away.

Once more into the unknown north away, till cold black night came down; then Yan sought out a sheltered spot and made a tiny, redman's fire. As Chaska had taught him long ago—'Big fire for fool'.

When the lad curled up to sleep he felt a vague wish to turn three times like a dog, and a well-defined wish that he had fur on his face and a bushy tail to lay around his freezing hands and feet, for it was a night of northern frost. Old Peboan was stalking on the snow. The stars seemed to crackle, so one could almost hear. The trees and earth were bursting with the awful frost. The ice on a near lake was rent all night by cracks that went whooping from shore to shore; and down between the hills there poured the cold that burns.

A prairie wolf came by in the night, but he did not howl or treat Yan like an outsider now. He gave a gentle, dog-like '*Woof, woof*', a sort of 'Oho! so you have come to it at last', and passed away. Toward morning the weather grew milder, but with the change there came a driving snow. The track was blotted out. Yan had heeded nothing else, and did not know where he was. After travelling an aimless mile or two he decided to make for Pine Creek, which ought to lie south-eastward. But which way was south-east? The

powdery snow was driven along through the air, blinding, stinging, burning. On all things near it was like smoke, and on farther things, a driving fog. But he made for a quaking asp grove, and there, sticking through the snow, he found a crosier golden rod, dead and dry, but still faithfully delivering its message, 'Yon is the north'. With course corrected, on he went, and, whenever in doubt, dug out this compass-flower, till the country dipped and Pine Creek lay below.

There was good camping here, the very spot indeed where, fifteen years before, Butler had camped on his Loneland Journey; but now the blizzard had ceased, so Yan spent the day hunting without seeing a track, and he spent the night as before, wishing that nature had been kinder to him in the matter of fur. During that first lone night his face and toes had been frozen and now bore burning sores. But still he kept on the chase, for something within had told him that the Grail was surely near. Next day a strange unreasoning guess sent him east across the creek in a deerless-looking barren land. Within half a mile he came on dim tracks made lately in the storm. He followed, and soon found where six deer had lain at rest, and among them a great broad bed and a giant track that only one could have made. The track was almost fresh, the sign unfrozen still. 'Within a mile,' he thought. But within a hundred yards there loomed up on a fog-wrapped hillside five heads with ears regardant, and at that moment, too, there rose up from the snowy top a great form like a blasted trunk with two dead boughs still on. But they had seen him first, and before the deadly gun could play, six beacons waved and a friendly hill had screened them from its power.

The Sandhill Stag had gathered his brood again, yet now that the murderer was on the track once more he scattered them as before. But there was only one track for Yan.

At last the chase led away to the great dip of Pine Creek —a mile-wide flat, with a long dense thicket down the middle.

'There is where he is hiding and watching now, but there he will not rest,' said the something within, and Yan kept out of sight and watched; after half an hour a dark spot left the willow belt and wandered up the farther hill. When he was well out of sight over the hill Yan ran across the valley and stalked around to get the trail on the down-wind side. He found it, and there learned that the Stag was as wise as he—he had climbed a good lookout and watched his back trail, then seeing Yan crossing the flat, his track went swiftly bounding, bounding. . . .

The Stag knew just how things stood; a single match to a finish now, and he led away for a new region. But Yan was learning something he had often heard—that the swiftest deer can be run down by a hardy man; for he was as fresh as ever, but the great Stag's bounds were shortening, he was surely tiring out, he must throw off the hunter now, or he is lost.

He often mounted a high hill to scan the white world for his foe, and the after-trail was a record of what he learned or feared. At last his trail came to a sudden end. This was a mystery until long study showed how he had returned backward on his own track for a hundred yards, then bounded aside to fly in another direction. Three times he did this, and then passed through an aspen thicket and, returning, lay down in this thicket near his own track, so that in following, Yan must pass where the Stag could smell and hear him long before the trail brought the hunter over-close.

All these doublings and many more like them were patiently unravelled and the shortening bounds were straightened out once more till, as daylight waned, the tracks seemed to grow stale and the bounds again grow long. After a little, Yan became wholly puzzled, so he stopped right there and spent another wretched night. Next day at dawn he worked it out.

He found he had been running the trail he had already run. With a long hark-back, the doubt was cleared. The desperate Stag had joined on to his old track and bounded

aside at length to let the hunter follow the cold scent. But the join-on was found and the real trail read, and the tale that it told was of a great Stag wearing out, too tired to eat too scared to sleep, with a tireless hunter after.

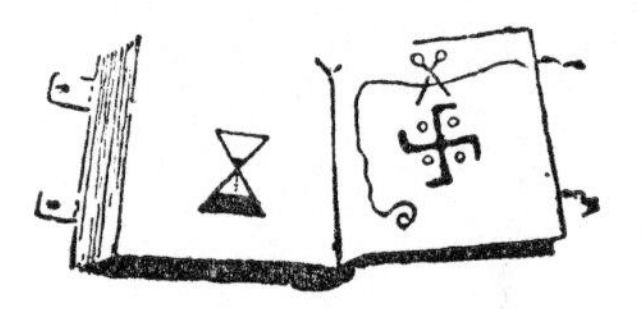

VIII

A LAST long follow brought the hunt back to familiar ground—a marsh-encompassed tract of woods with three ways in. There was the deer's trail entering. Yan felt he would not come out there, for he knew his foe was following. So swiftly and silently the hunter made for the second road on the down-wind side, and having hung his coat and sash there on a swaying sapling, he hastened to the third way out, and hid. After a while, seeing nothing, Yan gave the low call that the jaybird gives when there's danger abroad in the woods.

All deer take guidance from the jay, and away off in the encompassed woods Yan saw the great Stag with wavering ears go up a high lookout. A low whistle turned him to a statue, but he was far away with many a twig between. For some seconds he stood sniffing the wind and gazing with his back to his foe, watching the back trail, where so long his enemy had been, but never dreaming of that enemy in ambush ahead. Then the breeze set the coat on the sapling a-fluttering. The Stag quickly quit the hillock, not leaping or crashing through the brush—he had years ago got past that—but, silent and weasel-like threading the maze, he disappeared. Yan crouched in the willow thicket and strained

his every sense and tried to train his ears for keener watching. A twig ticked in the copse that he was in. Yan slowly rose with nerve and sense at tightest tense, the gun in line—and as he rose, there also rose, but fifteen feet away, a wondrous pair of bronze and ivory horns, a royal head, a noble form behind it, and face to face they stood, Yan and the Sandhill Stag. At last—at last, his life was in Yan's hands. The Stag flinched not, but stood and gazed with those great ears and mournful, truthful eyes, and the rifle leaped but sank again, for the Stag stood still and calmly looked him in the eyes, and Yan felt the prickling fading from his scalp, his clenched teeth eased, his limbs, bent as to spring, relaxed and manlike stood erect.

'*Shoot, shoot, shoot now! This is what you have toiled for,*' said a faint and fading voice, and spoke no more.

But Yan remembered the night when he, himself run down, had turned to face the hunting wolves, he remembered too that night when the snow was red with crime, and now between him and the other there he dimly saw a vision of an agonizing, dying doe, with great sad eyes, that only asked, 'What harm have I done you?' A change came over him, and every thought of murder went from Yan as they gazed into each other's eyes—and hearts. Yan could not look him in the eyes and take his life, and different thoughts and a wholly different concept of the Stag, coming—coming—long coming—had come.

Oh, beautiful creature! One of our wise men has said, the body is the soul made visible. Is your spirit then so beautiful—as beautiful as wise? We have long stood as foes, hunter and hunted, but now that is changed and we stand face to face, fellow creatures looking in each other's eyes, not knowing each other's speech—but know ing motives and feelings. Now I understand you as I never did before; surely you at least in part understand me. For your life is at last in my power, yet you have no fear. I knew of a deer once, that, run down by the hounds, sought safety with the hunter, and he saved it—and you also I have run down and you boldly seek safety with me. Yes! You are as wise as you are beautiful, for I will never harm a hair of you. We are brothers, oh, bounding Blacktail! Only I am the elder and stronger, and if only my strength could always be at hand to save you, you would never come to harm. Go now, without fear, to range the piney hills; never more shall I follow your trail with the wild wolf rampant in my heart. Less and less as I grow do I see in your race mere flying marks, or butcher-meat. We have grown, Little Brother, and learned many things that you know not, but you have many a precious sense that is wholly hidden from us. Go now without fear of me.

'I may never see you again. But if only you would come sometimes and look me in the eyes and make me feel as you have done today, you would drive the wild beast wholly from my heart, and then the veil would be a little drawn and I should know more of the things that wise men have prayed for knowledge of. And yet I feel it never will be—I have found the Grail. I have learned what Buddha learned. I shall never see you again. Farewell.'

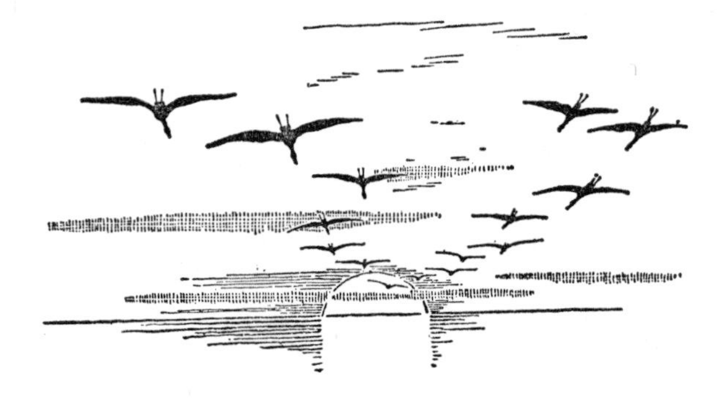

Johnny Bear

I

JOHNNY was a queer little bear cub that lived with Grumpy, his mother, in the Yellowstone Park. They were among the many bears that found a desirable home in the country about the Fountain Hotel.

The steward of the hotel had ordered the kitchen garbage to be dumped in an open glade of the surrounding forest, thus providing, throughout the season, a daily feast for the bears, and their numbers have increased each year since the law of the land has made the Park a haven of refuge where no wild thing may be harmed. They have accepted man's peace-offering, and many of them have become so well known to the hotel men that they have received names suggested by their looks or ways. Slim Jim was a very long-legged thin Black Bear; Snuffy was a Black Bear that looked as though he had been singed; Fatty was a very fat, lazy bear that always lay down to eat; the twins were two half-grown ragged specimens that always came and went together. But Grumpy and Little Johnny were the best known of them all.

Grumpy was the biggest and fiercest of the Black Bears, and Johnny, apparently her only son, was a peculiarly tiresome little cub, for he seemed never to cease either grumbling or whining. This probably meant that he was sick, for a healthy little bear does not grumble all the time, any more than a healthy child. And indeed Johnny looked sick; he was the most miserable specimen in the Park. His whole appearance suggested dyspepsia; and this I quite understood when I saw the awful mixtures he would eat at that garbage-heap. Anything at all that he fancied he would try. And his mother allowed him to do as he pleased; so, after all, it was chiefly her fault, for she should not have permitted such things.

Johnny had only three good legs, his coat was faded and mangy, his limbs were thin and his ears and paunch were disproportionately large. Yet his mother thought the world of him. She was evidently convinced that he was a little beauty and the prince of all bears, so of course she quite spoiled him. She was always ready to get into trouble on his account, and he was always delighted to lead her there. Although such a wretched little failure, Johnny was far from being a fool, for he usually knew just what he wanted and how to get it, if teasing his mother could carry the point.

II

It was the summer of 1897 that I made their acquaintance. I was in the Park to study the home life of the animals, and had been told that in the woods, near the Fountain Hotel, I could see bears at any time, which of course I scarcely believed. But on stepping out of the back door five minutes after arriving I came face to face with a large Black Bear and her two cubs.

I stopped short, not a little startled. The bears also stopped and sat up to look at me. Then Mother Bear made a curious short '*Koff Koff*', and looked toward a near pine tree. The cubs seemed to know what she meant, for they ran to this tree and scrambled up like two little monkeys, and when safely aloft they sat like small boys, holding on with their hands while their little black legs dangled in the air, and waited to see what was to happen down below.

The Mother Bear, still on her hind legs, came slowly toward me, and I began to feel very uncomfortable indeed, for she stood about six feet high in her stockings and had apparently never heard of the magical power of the human eye.

I had not even a stick to defend myself with, and when she gave a low growl I was about to retreat to the hotel, although previously assured that the bears have always kept their truce with man. However, just at this turning-point the old one stopped, now but thirty feet away, and continued to survey me calmly. She seemed in doubt for a minute, but evidently made up her mind that, 'although that human thing might be all right, she would take no chances for her little ones'.

She looked up to her two hopefuls and gave a peculiar whining '*Er-r-r Er-r*', whereupon they, like obedient children, jumped as at the word of command. There was nothing about them heavy or bear-like as commonly understood; lightly they swung from bough to bough till they dropped to the ground, and all went off together into the woods. I was much tickled by the prompt obedience of the little bears. As soon as their mother told them to do something they did it. They did not even offer a suggestion. But I also found out that there was a good reason for it, for had they not done as she had told them they would have got such a spanking as would have made them howl.

This was a delightful peep into bear home life, and would have been well worth coming for if the insight had ended there. But my friends in the hotel said that that was not the best place for bears. I should go to the garbage-heap, a quarter-mile off in the forest. There, they said, I surely could see as many bears as I wished (which was absurd of them).

Early the next morning I went to this Bears' Banqueting Hall, in the pines, and hid in the nearest bushes.

Before very long a large Black Bear came quietly out of the woods to the pile, and began turning over the garbage and feeding. He was very nervous, sitting up and looking about at each slight sound, or running away a few yards when startled by some trifle. At length he cocked his ears and galloped off into the pines, as another Black Bear appeared. He also behaved in the same timid manner, and at last ran away when I shook the bushes in trying to get a better view.

At the outset I myself had been very nervous, for of course no man is allowed to carry weapons in the Park; but the timidity of these bears reassured me, and thenceforth I forgot everything in the interest of seeing the great shaggy creatures in their home life.

Soon I realized I could not get the close insight I wished from that bush, as it was seventy-five yards from the garbage-pile. There was none nearer; so I did the only thing left to do: I went to the garbage-pile itself and, digging a hole big enough to hide in, remained there all day long, with cabbage-stalks, old potato-peelings, tomato cans, and carrion piled up in odorous heaps around me. Notwithstanding the opinions of countless flies, it was not an attractive place. Indeed it was so unfragrant that at night, when I returned to the hotel, I was not allowed to come in until after I had changed my clothes in the woods.

It had been a trying ordeal, but I surely did see bears that day. If I may reckon it a new bear each time one came, I must have seen over forty. But of course it was not, for the bears were coming and going. And yet I am certain of this: there were at least thirteen bears, for I had thirteen about me at one time.

All that day I used my sketch-book and journal. Every bear that came was duly noted; and this process soon began to give the desired insight into their ways and personalities.

Many unobservant persons think

and say that all Negroes, or all Chinamen, as well as all animals of a kind, look alike.

But just as surely as each human being differs from the next, so surely each animal is different from its fellow; otherwise how would the old ones know their mates or the little ones their mother, as they certainly do? These feasting bears gave a good illustration of this, for each had its individuality; no two were quite alike in appearance or in character.

This curious fact also appeared: I could hear the woodpeckers pecking over one hundred yards away in the woods, as well as the chickadees chickadeeing, the blue-jays blue-jaying, and even the squirrels scampering across the leafy forest floor; and yet I *did not hear one of these bears come*. Their huge padded feet always went down in exactly the right spot to break no stick, to rustle no leaf, showing how perfectly they had learned the art of going in silence through the woods.

III

All morning the bears came and went or wandered near my hiding-place without discovering me; and, except for one or two brief quarrels, there was nothing very exciting to note. But about three in the afternoon it became more lively.

There were then four large bears feeding on the heap. In the middle was Fatty, sprawling at full length as he feasted, a picture of placid ursine content, puffing just a little at times as he strove to save himself the trouble of moving by darting out his tongue like a long red serpent, farther and farther, in quest of the titbits just beyond claw reach.

Behind him Slim Jim was puzzling over the anatomy and attributes of an ancient lobster. It was something outside his experience, but the principle, 'In case of doubt take the trick', is well known in Bearland, and settled the difficulty.

The other two were clearing out fruit tins with marvellous dexterity. One supple paw would hold the tin while the long tongue would dart again and again through the narrow opening, avoiding the sharp edges, yet cleaning out the can to the last taste of its sweetness.

This pastoral scene lasted long enough to be sketched, but was ended abruptly. My eye caught a movement on the hill top whence all the bears had come, and out stalked a very large Black Bear with a tiny cub. It was Grumpy and Little Johnny.

The old bear stalked down the slope toward the feast, and Johnny hitched alongside, grumbling as he came, his mother watching him as solicitously as ever a hen did her single chick. When they were within thirty yards of the garbage-heap Grumpy turned to her son and said something which, judging from its effect, must have meant: 'Johnny, my child, I think you had better stay here while I go and chase those fellows away.'

Johnny obediently waited; but he wanted to *see*, so he sat up on his hind legs with eyes agog and ears a-cock.

Grumpy came striding along with dignity, uttering warning growls as she approached the four bears. They were too much engrossed to pay any heed to the fact that yet another one of them was coming, till Grumpy, now within fifteen feet, let out a succession of loud coughing sounds and charged into them. Strange to say, they did not pretend to face her, but, as soon as they saw who it was, scattered and all fled for the woods.

Slim Jim could safely trust his heels, and the other two were not far behind; but poor Fatty, puffing hard and waddling like any other very fat creature, got along but slowly and, unluckily for him, he fled in the direction of Johnny, so that Grumpy overtook him in a few bounds and gave him a couple of sound slaps in the rear which, if they did not accelerate his pace, at least made him bawl, and saved him by changing his direction. Grumpy, now left alone in possession of the feast, turned towards her son and uttered the whining '*Er-r-r Er-r-r Er-r-r-r*'. Johnny responded eagerly. He came 'hoppity-hop' on his three good legs as fast as he could and, joining her on the garbage, they began to have such a good time that Johnny actually ceased grumbling.

He had evidently been there before now, for he seemed to know quite well the staple kinds of canned goods. One might almost have supposed that he had learned the brands, for a lobster tin had no charm for him as long as he could find those that once were filled with jam. Some of the tins gave him much trouble, as he was too greedy or too clumsy to escape being scratched by the sharp edges. One seductive fruit tin had a hole so large that he found he could force his head into it, and for a few minutes his joy was full as he licked into all the farthest corners. But when he tried to draw his head out his sorrows began, for he found himself caught. He could not get out, and he scratched and screamed like any other spoiled child, giving his mother no end of concern, although she seemed not to know how to help him. When at length he got the tin off his head he revenged himself by hammering it with his paws till it was perfectly flat.

A large syrup can made him happy for a long time. It had had a lid, so that the hole was round and smooth; but it was not big enough to admit his head, and he could not touch its riches with his tongue stretched out its longest. He soon hit on a plan, however. Putting in his little black arm, he churned it around, then drew out and licked it clean; and while he licked one he got the other one ready; and he did this again and again, until the can was as clean inside as when first it had left the factory.

A broken mousetrap seemed to puzzle him. He clutched it between his fore-paws, their strong inturn being

sympathetically reflected in his hind feet, and held it firmly for study. The cheesy smell about it was decidedly good, but the thing responded in such an uncanny way, when he slapped it, that he kept back a cry for help only by the exercise of unusual self-control. After gravely inspecting it, with his head first on this side and then on that, and his lips puckered into a little tube, he submitted it to the same punishment as that meted out to the refractory fruit tin, and was rewarded by discovering a nice little bit of cheese in the very heart of the culprit.

Johnny had evidently never heard of ptomaine poisoning, for nothing came amiss. After the jams and fruits gave out he turned his attention to the lobster and sardine cans, and was not appalled by even the army beef. His paunch grew quite balloon-like, and from much licking his arms looked thin and shiny, as though he was wearing black silk gloves.

IV

It occurred to me that I might now be in a really dangerous place. For it is one thing surprising a bear that has no family responsibilities, and another sitirring up a bad-tempered old mother by frightening her cub.

'Supposing', I thought, 'that cranky Little Johnny should wander over to this end of the garbage and find me in the hole; he will at once set up a squall, and his mother of course will think I am hurting him and, without giving me a chance to explain, may forget the rules of the Park and make things very unpleasant.'

Luckily all the jam pots were at Johnny's end; he stayed by them and Grumpy stayed by him. At length he noticed that his mother had a better tin than any he could find, and as he ran whining to take it from her he chanced to glance away up the slope. There he saw something that made him sit up and utter a curious little '*Koff Koff Koff Koff*'.

His mother turned quickly, and sat up to see what the

child was looking at. I followed their gaze, and there, oh, horrors! was an enormous Grizzly Bear. He was a monster; he looked like a fur-clad omnibus coming through the trees.

Johnny set up a whine at once and got behind his mother. She uttered a deep growl, and all her back hair stood on end. Mine did too, but I kept as still as possible.

With stately tread the Grizzly came on. His vast shoulders sliding along his sides, and his silvery robe swaying at each tread, like the trappings on an elephant, gave an impression of power that was appalling.

Johnny began to whine more loudly, and I fully sympathized with him now, though I did not join in. After a moment's hesitation Grumpy turned to her noisy cub and said something that sounded to me like two or three short coughs—'*Koff Koff Koff*'. But I imagine that she really said: 'My child, I think you had better get up that tree, while I go and drive the brute away.'

At any rate, that was what Johnny did, and this what she set out to do. But Johnny had no notion of missing any fun. He wanted to *see* what was going to happen. So he did not rest contented where he was hidden in the thick branches of the pine, but combined safety with view by climbing to the topmost branch that would bear him, and there, sharp against the sky, he squirmed about and squealed aloud in excitement. The branch was so small that it bent under his weight, swaying this way and that as he shifted about, and every moment I expected to see it snap off. If it had been broken when swaying my way, Johnny would certainly have fallen on me, and this would probably have resulted in bad feelings between myself and his mother; but the limb was tougher than it looked, or perhaps Johnny had had plenty of experience, for he neither lost his hold nor broke the branch.

Meanwhile Grumpy stalked out to meet the Grizzly. She stood as high as she could and set all her bristles on end; then, growling and chopping her teeth, she faced him.

The Grizzly, so far as I could see, took no notice of her.

He came striding toward the feast as though alone. But when Grumpy got within twelve feet of him she uttered a succession of short, coughy roars and, charging, gave him a tremendous blow on the ear. The Grizzly was surprised; but he replied with a left-hander that knocked her over like a sack of hay.

Nothing daunted, but doubly furious, she jumped up and rushed at him.

Then they clinched and rolled over and over, whacking and pounding, snorting and growling, and making no end of dust and rumpus. But above all their noise I could clearly hear Little Johnny, yelling at the top of his voice and evidently encouraging his mother to go right in and finish the Grizzly at once.

Why the Grizzly did not break her in two I could not understand. After a few minutes' struggle, during which I could see nothing but dust and dim flying legs, the two separated as by mutual consent—perhaps the regulation time was up—and for a while they stood glaring at each other, Grumpy at least much winded.

The Grizzly would have dropped the matter right there. He did not wish to fight. He had no idea of troubling himself about Johnny. All he wanted was a quiet meal. But no! The moment he took one step toward the garbage-pile (that is, as Grumpy thought, toward Johnny) she went at him again. But this time the Grizzly was ready for her. With one blow he knocked her off her feet and sent her crashing on to a huge upturned pine-root. She was fairly staggered this time. The force of the blow, and the rude reception of the rooty antlers, seemed to take all the fight out of her. She scrambled over and tried to escape. But the Grizzly was mad now. He meant to punish her, and dashed around the root. For a minute they kept up a dodging chase about it; but Grumpy was quicker of foot, and somehow always

managed to keep the root between herself and her foe, while Johnny, safe in the tree, continued to take an intense and uproarious interest.

At length, seeing he could not catch her that way, the Grizzly sat up on his haunches; and while he doubtless was planning a new move old Grumpy saw her chance and, making a dash, got away from the root and up to the top of the tree where Johnny was perched.

Johnny came down a little way to meet her, or perhaps so that the tree might not break off with the additional weight. Having photographed this interesting group from my hiding-place, I thought I must get a closer picture at any price, and for the first time in the day's proceedings I jumped out of the hole and ran under the tree. This move proved a great mistake, for here the thick lower boughs came between, and I could see nothing at all of the bears at the top.

I was close to the trunk, and was peering about and seeking for a chance to use the camera, when old Grumpy began to come down, chopping her teeth and uttering her threatening cough at me. While I stood in doubt, I heard a voice far behind me calling:

'Say, mister! You better look out; that ole b'ar is liable to hurt you.'

I turned to see the cowboy of the hotel on his horse. He had been riding after the cattle, and chanced to pass near just as events were moving quickly.

'Do you know these bears?' said I as he rode up.

'Wall, I reckon I do,' said he. 'That there little one up top is Johnny; he's a little crank. An' the big un is Grumpy, she's a big crank. She's mighty onreliable gen'relly, but she's always strictly ugly when Johnny hollers like that.'

'I should much like to get her picture when she comes down,' said I.

'Tell ye what I'll do: I'll stay by on the pony, an' if she goes to bother you I reckon I can keep her off,' said the man.

He accordingly stood by as Grumpy slowly came down from branch to branch, growling and threatening. But when she neared the ground she kept on the far side of the trunk, and finally slipped down and ran into the woods, without the slightest pretence of carrying out any of her dreadful threats. Thus Johnny was again left alone. He climbed up to his old perch and resumed his monotonous whining: '*Wah! Wah! Wah!*' ('Oh dear! Oh dear! Oh dear!').

I got the camera ready, and was arranging deliberately to take his picture in his favourite and peculiar attitude for threnodic song, when all at once he began craning his neck and yelling as he had done during the fight.

I looked where his nose pointed, and here was the Grizzly coming on straight toward me—not charging, but striding along, as though he meant to come the whole distance.

I said to my cowboy friend: 'Do you know this bear?'

He replied: 'Wall! I reckon I do. That's the ole Grizzly. He's the biggest b'ar in the Park. He gen'relly minds his own business, but he ain't scared o' nothin'; an' today, ye see, he's been scrappin', so he's liable to be ugly.'

'I would like to take his picture,' said I; 'and if you will help me I am willing to take some chances on it.'

'All right,' said he with a grin. 'I'll stand by on the horse, an' if he charges you I'll charge him; an' I kin knock him down once, but I can't do it twice. You better have your tree picked out.'

As there was only one tree to pick out, and that was the one that Johnny was in, the prospect was not alluring. I imagined myself scrambling up there next to Johnny, and then Johnny's mother coming up after me, with the Grizzly below to catch me when Grumpy should throw me down.

The Grizzly came on, and I snapped him at forty yards, then again at twenty yards; and still he came quietly toward me. I sat down on the garbage and made ready. Eighteen yards—sixteen yards—twelve yards—eight yards, and still he came, while the pitch of Johnny's protests kept rising proportionately. Finally at five yards he stopped, and swung his huge bearded head to one side, to see what was making that aggravating row in the tree top, giving me a profile view, and I snapped the camera. At the click he turned on me with a thunderous

G—R—O—W—L!

and I sat still and trembling, wondering if my last moment had come. For a second he glared at me, and I could note the little green electric lamp in each of his eyes. Then he slowly turned and picked up—a large tomato can.

'Goodness!' I thought. 'Is he going to throw *that* at me?' But he deliberately licked it out, dropped it and took another, paying thenceforth no heed whatever either to me or to Johnny, evidently considering us equally beneath his notice.

I backed slowly and respectfully out of his royal presence, leaving him in possession of the garbage, while Johnny kept on caterwauling from his safety perch.

What became of Grumpy the rest of that day I do not know. Johnny, after bewailing for a time, realized that there was no sympathetic hearer of his cries, and therefore very sagaciously stopped them. Having no mother now to plan for him, he began to plan for himself, and at once proved that he was better stuff than he seemed. After watching with a look of profound cunning on his little black face, and waiting till the Grizzly was some distance away, he silently slipped down behind the trunk and, despite his three-leggedness, ran like a hare to the next tree, never stopping to breathe till he was on its topmost bough. For he was thoroughly convinced that the only object that the Grizzly had in life was to kill him, and he seemed quite aware that his enemy could not climb a tree.

Another long and safe survey of the Grizzly, who really paid no heed to him whatever, was followed by another dash for the next tree, varied occasionally by a cunning feint to mislead the foe. So he went dashing from tree to tree and climbing each to its very top, although it might be but ten feet from the last, till he disappeared in the woods. After perhaps ten minutes his voice again came floating on the breeze, the habitual querulous whining which told me he had found his mother and had resumed his customary appeal to her sympathy.

V

It is quite a common thing for bears to spank their cubs when they need it, and if Grumpy had disciplined Johnny this way it would have saved them both a deal of worry.

Perhaps not a day passed that summer without Grumpy getting into trouble on Johnny's account. But of all these numerous occasions the most ignominious was shortly after the affair with the Grizzly.

I first heard the story from three bronzed mountaineers. As they were very sensitive about having their word doubted, and very good shots with the revolver, I believed every word they told me, especially when afterward fully endorsed by the Park authorities.

It seemed that of all the tinned goods on the pile the nearest to Johnny's taste were marked with a large purple plum. This conclusion he had arrived at only after most exhaustive study. The very odour of those plums in Johnny's nostrils was the equivalent of ecstasy. So when it

came about one day that the cook of the hotel baked a huge batch of plum tarts, the telltale wind took the story afar into the woods, where it was wafted by way of Johnny's nostrils to his very soul.

Of course Johnny was whimpering at the time. His mother was busy 'washing his face and combing his hair', so he had double cause for whimpering. But the smell of the tarts thrilled him; he jumped up, and when his mother tried to hold him he squalled—and, I am afraid, he bit her. She should have cuffed him, but she did not. She only gave a disapproving growl and followed to see that he came to no harm.

With his little black nose in the wind, Johnny led straight for the kitchen. He took the precaution, however, of climbing from time to time to the very top of a pine tree lookout to take an observation, while Grumpy stayed below.

Thus they came close to the kitchen, and there, in the last tree, Johnny's courage as a leader gave out, so he remained aloft and expressed his hankering for tarts in a woebegone wail.

It is not likely that Grumpy knew exactly what her son was crying for. But it is sure that, as soon as she showed an inclination to go back into the pines, Johnny protested in such an outrageous and heartrending screeching that his mother simply could not leave him, and he showed no sign of coming down to be led away.

Grumpy herself was fond of plum jam. The odour was now, of course, very strong and proportionately alluring; so Grumpy followed it somewhat cautiously up to the kitchen door.

There was nothing surprising about this. The rule of 'live and let live' is so strictly enforced in the Park that the bears often come to the kitchen door for pickings and, on getting something, they go quietly back to the woods. Doubtless Johnny and Grumpy would each have got their tart but that a new factor appeared in the case.

That week the hotel people had brought a new cat from the East. She was not much more than a kitten, but still had a litter of her own, and at the moment that Grumpy reached the door the cat and her family were sunning themselves on the top step. Pussy opened her eyes to see this huge shaggy monster towering above her.

The cat had never before seen a bear—she had not been there long enough; she did not know even what a bear was. She knew what a dog was, and here was a bigger, more awful bobtailed black dog than ever she had dreamed of coming right at her. Her first thought was to fly for her life, but her next was for the kittens. She must take care of them. She must at least cover their retreat. So, like a brave little mother, she braced herself on that doorstep and, spreading her back, her claws, her tail and everything she had to spread, she screamed out at that bear an unmistakable order to

STOP!

The language must have been 'cat', but the meaning was clear to the bear; for those who saw it maintain stoutly that Grumpy not only stopped, but she also conformed to the custom of the country and in token of surrender held up her hands.

However, the position she thus took made her so high that the cat seemed tiny in the distance below. Old Grumpy had faced a Grizzly once, and was she now to be held up by a miserable little spike-tailed skunk no bigger than a mouthful? She was ashamed of herself, especially when a wail from Johnny smote on her ear and reminded her of her plain duty, as well as supplied his usual moral support.

So she dropped down on her front feet to proceed.

Again the cat shrieked, 'STOP!'

But Grumpy ignored the command. A scared mew from a kitten nerved the cat, and she launched her ultimatum, which ultimatum was herself. Eighteen sharp claws, a mouthful of keen teeth, had Pussy, and she worked them all with a desperate will when she landed on Grumpy's bare, bald, sensitive nose, just the spot of all where the bear could not stand it, and then worked backward to a point outside the sweep of Grumpy's claws. After one or two vain attempts to shake the spotted fury off, old Grumpy did just as most creatures would have done in the circumstances: she turned tail and bolted out of the enemy's country into her own woods.

But Pussy's fighting blood was up. She was not content with repelling the enemy; she wanted to inflict a crushing defeat, to achieve an absolute and final rout. And however fast old Grumpy might go, it did not count, for the cat was still on top, working her teeth and claws like a little demon. Grumpy, always erratic, now became panic-stricken. The trail of the pair was flecked with tufts of long black hair, and there was even bloodshed (in the fiftieth degree). Honour surely was satisfied, but Pussy was not. Round and round they had gone in the mad race. Grumpy was frantic, absolutely humiliated and ready to make any terms; but Pussy seemed deaf to her cough-like yelps, and no one knows how far the cat might have ridden that day had not Johnny unwittingly put a new idea into his mother's head by bawling in his best style from the top of his last tree, which tree Grumpy made for and scrambled up.

This was so clearly the enemy's country and in view of his reinforcements that the cat wisely decided to follow no farther. She jumped from the climbing bear to the ground, and then mounted sentry guard below, marching around with tail in the air, daring that bear to come down. Then the kittens came out and sat around and enjoyed it all hugely.

And the mountaineers assured me that the bears would have been kept up the tree till they were starved, had not the cook of the hotel come out and called off his cat—although this statement was not among those vouched for by the officers of the Park.

VI

THE last time I saw Johnny was in the top of a tree, bewailing his unhappy lot as usual, while his mother was dashing about among the pines, 'with a chip on her shoulder', seeking for someone—anyone—that she could punish for Johnny's sake, provided, of course, that it was not a big Grizzly or a Mother Cat.

This was early in August, but there were not lacking symptoms of change in old Grumpy. She was always reckoned 'onsartain', and her devotion to Johnny seemed subject to her characteristic. This perhaps accounted for the fact that, when the end of the month was near, Johnny would sometimes spend half a day in the top of some tree, alone, miserable and utterly unheeded.

The last chapter of his history came to pass after I had left the region. One day at grey dawn he was tagging along behind his mother as she prowled in the rear of the hotel. A newly hired Irish girl was already astir in the kitchen. On looking out, she saw (as she thought) a calf where it should not be, and ran to shoo it away. That open kitchen door still held unmeasured terrors for Grumpy, and she ran in such alarm that Johnny caught the infection, and not being able to keep up with her, he made for the nearest tree, which unfortunately turned out to be a post, and soon—too soon—he arrived at its top, some seven feet from the ground, and there poured forth his woes on the chilly morning air, while Grumpy apparently felt justified in continuing her flight alone. When the girl came near and saw that she had treed some wild animal, she was as much frightened as her victim. But others of the kitchen staff appeared and, recognizing the vociferous Johnny, they decided to make him a prisoner.

A collar and chain were brought, and after a struggle, during which several of the men got well scratched, the collar was buckled on Johnny's neck and the chain made fast to the post.

When he found that he was held, Johnny was simply too mad to scream. He bit and scratched and tore till he was tired out. Then he lifted up his voice again to call his mother. She did appear once or twice in the distance, but could not make up her mind to face that cat, so disappeared, and Johnny was left to his fate.

He put in the most of that day in alternate struggling and crying. Toward evening he was worn out, and glad to accept the meal that was brought by Norah, who felt herself called on to play mother, since she had chased his own mother away.

When night came it was very cold; but Johnny nearly froze at the top of the post before he would come down and accept the warm bed provided at the bottom.

During the days that followed, Grumpy came often to the garbage-heap, but soon apparently succeeded in forgetting all about her son. He was daily tended by Norah and received all his meals from her. He also received something else; for one day he scratched her when she brought his food and she very properly spanked him till he squealed. For a few hours he sulked; he was not used to such treatment. But hunger subdued him, and thenceforth he held his new guardian in wholesome respect. She too began to

take an interest in the poor motherless little wretch, and within a fortnight Johnny showed signs of developing a new character. He was much less noisy. He still expressed his hunger in a whining '*Er-r-r Er-r-r Er-r-r*', but he rarely squealed now, and his unruly outbursts entirely ceased.

By the third week of September the change was still more marked. Utterly abandoned by his own mother, all his interest had centred in Norah, and she had fed and spanked him into an exceedingly well-behaved little bear. Sometimes she would allow him a taste of freedom, and he then showed his bias by making, not for the woods, but for the kitchen where she was, and following her around on his hind legs. Here also he made the acquaintance of that dreadful cat; but Johnny had a powerful friend now, and Pussy finally became reconciled to the black woolly interloper.

As the hotel was to be closed in October there was talk of turning Johnny loose or of sending him to the Washington Zoo; but Norah had claims that she would not forego.

When the frosty nights of late September came, Johnny had greatly improved in his manners, but he had also developed a bad cough. An examination of his lame leg had shown that the weakness was not in the foot, but much more deeply seated, perhaps in the hip, and that meant a feeble and tottering constitution.

He did not get fat, as do most Bears in fall; indeed he continued to fail. His little round belly shrank in, his cough became worse, and one morning he was found very sick and shivering in his bed by the post. Norah brought him indoors, where the warmth helped him so much that thenceforth he lived in the kitchen.

For a few days he seemed better, and his old-time pleasure in *seeing things* revived. The great blazing fire in the range particularly appealed to him, and made him sit up in his old attitude when the opening of the door brought the wonder to view. After a week he lost interest even in that, and drooped more and more each day. Finally not the most exciting noises or scenes around him could stir up his old fondness for seeing what was going on.

He coughed a good deal, too, and seemed wretched, except when in Norah's lap. Here he would cuddle up contentedly, and whine most miserably when she had to set him down again in his basket.

A few days before the closing of the hotel, he refused his usual breakfast, and whined softly till Norah took him in her lap; then he feebly snuggled up to her, and his soft '*Er-r-r Er-r-r*' grew fainter, till it ceased. Half an hour later, when she laid him down to go about her work, Little Johnny had lost the last trace of his anxiety to see and know what was going on.

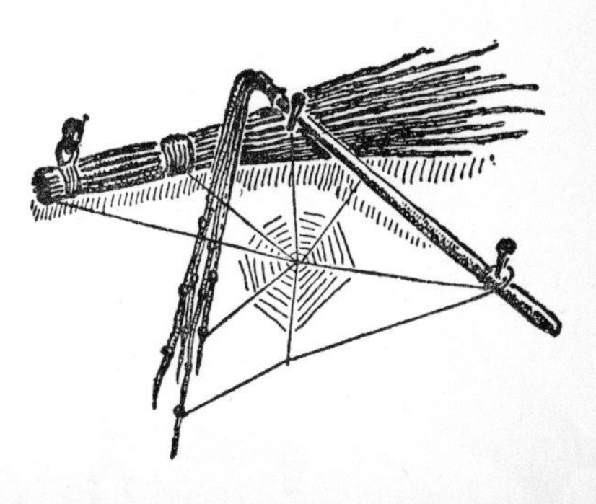

Tito

The Story of the Coyote that Learned How

I

A RAINDROP may deflect a thunderbolt, or a hair may ruin an empire, as surely as a spider-web once turned the history of Scotland; and, if it had not been for one little pebble, this history of Tito might never have happened.

That pebble was lying on a trail in the Dakota Badlands, and one hot dark night it lodged in the foot of a horse that was ridden by a tipsy cowboy. The man got off, as a matter of habit, to know what was laming his horse. But he left the reins on its neck instead of on the ground, and the horse, taking advantage of this technicality, ran off in the darkness. Then the cowboy, realizing that he was afoot, lay down in a hollow under some buffalo bushes and slept the loggish sleep of the befuddled.

The golden beams of the early summer sun were leaping from top to top of the wonderful Badland Buttes when an old coyote might have been seen trotting homeward along the Garner's Creek Trail with a rabbit in her jaws to supply her family's breakfast.

Fierce war had for a long time been waged against the coyote kind by the cattlemen of Billings County. Traps, guns, poison and hounds had reduced their number nearly to zero, and the few survivors had learned the bitter need of caution at every step. But the destructive ingenuity of man

knew no bounds, and their numbers continued to dwindle.

The old coyote quit the trail very soon, for nothing that man has made is friendly. She skirted along a low ridge, then across a little hollow where grew a few buffalo bushes and, after a careful sniff at a very stale human trail-scent, she crossed another near ridge on whose sunny side was the home of her brood. Again she cautiously circled, peered about and sniffed, but finding no sign of danger, went down to the doorway and uttered a low '*woof-woof*'. Out of the den, beside a sage bush, there poured a procession of little coyotes, merrily tumbling over one another. Then, barking little barks and growling little puppy growls, they fell upon the feast that their mother had brought and gobbled and tussled while she looked on and enjoyed their joy.

Wolver Jake, the cowboy, had awakened from his chilly sleep about sunrise, in time to catch a glimpse of the coyote passing over the ridge. As soon as she was out of sight he got on his feet and went to the edge, there to witness the interesting scene of the family breakfasting and frisking about within a few yards of him, utterly unconscious of any danger.

But the only appeal the scene had to him lay in the fact that the county had set a price on every one of these coyotes' lives. So he got out his big ·45 navy revolver and, notwithstanding his shaky condition, he managed somehow to get a sight on the mother as she was caressing one of the little ones that had finished its breakfast, and shot her dead on the spot.

The terrified cubs fled into the den, and Jake, failing to kill another with his revolver, came forward, blocked up the hole with stones and, leaving the seven little prisoners quaking at the far end, set off on foot for the nearest ranch, cursing his faithless horse as he went.

In the afternoon he returned with his pard and tools for

digging. The little ones had cowered all day in the darkened hole, wondering why their mother did not come to feed them, wondering at the darkness and the change. But late that day they heard sounds at the door. Then light was again let in. Some of the less cautious young ones ran forward to meet their mother, but their mother was not there—only two great rough brutes that began tearing open their home.

After an hour or more the diggers came to the end of the den, and here were the woolly, bright-eyed little ones, all huddled in a pile at the farthest corner. Their innocent puppy faces and ways were not noticed by the huge enemy. One by one they were seized. A sharp blow, and each quivering limp form was thrown into a sack to be carried to the nearest magistrate who was empowered to pay the bounties.

Even at this age there was a certain individuality of character among the puppies. Some of them squealed and some of them growled when dragged out to die. One or two tried to bite. The one that had been slowest to comprehend the danger had been the last to retreat, and so was on top of the pile and therefore the first killed. The one that had first realized the peril had retreated first, and now crouched at the bottom of the pile. Coolly and remorselessly the others were killed one by one, and then this prudent little puppy was seen to be the last of the family. It lay perfectly still, even when touched, its eyes being half closed as, guided by instinct, it tried to 'play possum'. One of the men picked it up. It neither squealed nor resisted. Then Jake, realizing ever the importance of 'standing in with the boss', said: 'Say, let's keep that 'un for the children.' So the last of the family was thrown alive into the same bag with its dead brothers and, bruised and frightened, lay there very

still, understanding nothing, knowing only that after a long time of great noise and cruel jolting it was again half strangled by a grip on its neck and dragged out, where were a lot of creatures like the diggers.

These were really the inhabitants of the Chimney-pot Ranch, whose brand is the broad arrow; and among them were the children for whom the cub had been brought. The boss had no difficulty in getting Jake to accept the dollar that the cub coyote would have brought in bounty money, and his present was turned over to the children. In answer to their question, 'What is it?' a Mexican cowhand present said it was a Coyotito—that is, a 'little coyote', and this, afterward shortened to 'Tito', became the captive's name.

II

TITO was a pretty little creature, with woolly body, a puppy-like expression and a head that was singularly broad between the ears.

But as a children's pet she—for it proved to be a female—was not a success. She was distant and distrustful. She ate her food and seemed healthy, but never responded to friendly advances; never even learned to come out of the box when called. This was probably due to the fact that the kindness of the small children was offset by the roughness of the men and boys, who did not hesitate to drag her out by the chain when they wished to see her. On these occasions she would suffer in silence, playing possum, shamming dead, for she seemed to know that that was the best thing to do. But as soon as released she would once more retire into the darkest corner of her box, and watch her tormentors with eyes that, at the proper angle, showed a telling glint of green.

Among the children of the ranchmen was a thirteen-year-old boy. The fact that he grew up to be like his father, a kind, strong and thoughtful man, did not prevent him being, at this age, a shameless little brute.

Like all boys in that country, he practised lasso-throwing,

with a view to being a cowboy. Posts and stumps are uninteresting things to catch. His little brothers and sisters were under special protection of the Home Government. The dogs ran far away whenever they saw him coming with the rope in his hands. So he must needs practise on the unfortunate Coyotito. She soon learned that her only hope for peace was to hide in the kennel or, if thrown at when outside, to dodge the rope by lying as flat as possible on the ground. Thus Lincoln unwittingly taught the coyote the dangers and limitations of a rope, and so he proved a blessing in disguise—a very perfect disguise. When the coyote had thoroughly learned how to baffle the lasso the boy terror devised a new amusement. He got a large trap of the kind known as 'fox-size'. This he set in the dust as he had seen Jake set a wolf-trap, close to the kennel, and over it he scattered scraps of meat, in the most approved style for wolf-trapping. After a while Tito, drawn by the smell of the meat, came hungrily sneaking out toward it and almost immediately was caught in the trap by one foot. The boy terror was watching from a near hiding-place. He gave a wild Indian whoop of delight, then rushed forward to drag the coyote out of the box into which she had retreated. After some more delightful thrills of excitement and struggle he got his lasso on Tito's body and, helped by a younger brother, a most promising pupil, he succeeded in setting the coyote free from the trap before the grown-ups had discovered his amusement. One or two experiences like this taught her a mortal terror of traps. She soon learned the smell of the steel, and could detect and avoid it, no matter how cleverly Master Lincoln might bury it in the dust, while the younger brother screened the operation from the intended victim by holding his coat over the door of Tito's kennel.

One day the fastening of her chain gave way, and Tito went off in an uncertain fashion, trailing her chain behind her. But she was seen by one of the men, who fired a charge of bird-shot at her. The burning, stinging and surprise of it all caused her to retreat to the one place she knew, her own kennel. The chain was fastened again, and Tito added to her ideas this, a horror of guns and the smell of gunpowder; and this also, that the one safety from them is to 'lay low'.

There were yet other rude experiences in store for the captive.

Poisoning wolves was a topic of daily talk at the ranch, so it was not surprising that Lincoln should privately experiment on Coyotito. The deadly strychnine was too well guarded to be available. So Lincoln hid some 'Rough on Rats' in a piece of meat, threw it to the captive, and sat by to watch, as blithe and conscience-clear as any professor of chemistry trying a new combination.

Tito smelled the meat—everything had to be passed on by her nose. Her nose was in doubt. There was a good smell of meat, a familiar but unpleasant smell of human hands and a strange new odour, but not the odour of the trap; so she bolted the morsel. Within a few minutes she began to have fearful pains in her stomach, followed by cramps. Now in all the wolf tribe there is the instinctive habit to throw up anything that disagrees with them, and after a minute or two of suffering the coyote sought relief in this way; and to make it doubly sure she hastily gobbled some blades of grass, and in less than an hour was quite well again.

Lincoln had put in poison enough for a dozen coyotes. Had he put in less she could not have felt the pang till too late, but she recovered and never forgot that peculiar smell that means such awful after-pains. More than that, she was ready thenceforth to fly at once to the herbal cure that Nature had everywhere provided. An instinct of this kind grows quickly, once followed. It had taken minutes of suffering in the first place to drive her to the easement. Thenceforth, having learned, it was her first thought on feeling pain. The little miscreant did indeed succeed in having her swallow another bait with a small dose of poison, but she knew what to do now and had almost no suffering.

Later on a relative sent Lincoln a bull-terrier, and the new combination was a fresh source of spectacular interest for the boy, and of tribulation for the coyote. It all emphasized for her that old idea to 'lay low'—that is, to be quiet, unobtrusive and hide when danger is in sight. The grown-ups of the household at length forbade these persecutions, and the terrier was kept away from the little yard where the coyote was chained up.

It must not be supposed that, in all this, Tito was a sweet innocent victim. She had learned to bite. She had caught and killed several chickens by shamming sleep while they ventured to forage within the radius of her chain. And she had an inborn hankering to sing a morning and evening hymn, which procured for her many beatings. But she learned to shut up the moment her opening notes were followed by a rattle of doors or windows, for these sounds of human nearness had frequently been followed by a *bang* and a charge of bird-shot, which somehow did no serious harm, though it severely stung her hide. And these experiences all helped to deepen her terror of guns and of those who used them. The object of these musical outpourings was not clear. They happened usually at dawn or dusk, but sometimes a loud noise at high noon would set her going. The song consisted of a volley of short barks, mixed with doleful squalls that never failed to set the dogs astir in a responsive uproar, and once or twice had begotten a faraway answer from some wild coyote in the hills.

There was one little trick that she had developed which was purely instinctive—that is, an inherited habit. In the back end of her kennel she had a little cache of bones, and knew exactly where one or two lumps of unsavoury meat were buried within the radius of her chain, for a time of famine which never came. If anyone approached these hidden treasures she watched with anxious eyes, but made no other demonstration. If she saw that the meddler knew the exact place she took an early opportunity to secrete them elsewhere.

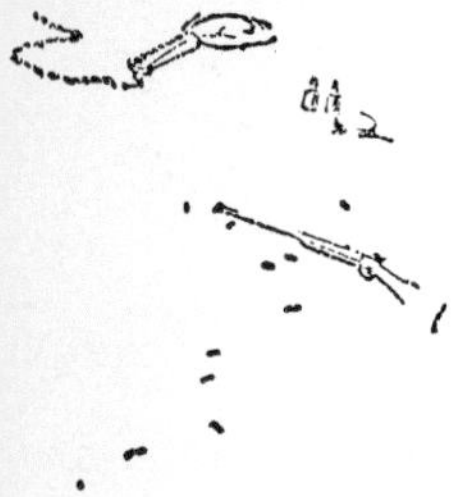

After a year of this life Tito had grown to full size, and had learned many things that her wild kinsmen could not have learned without losing their lives in doing it. She knew and feared traps. She had learned to avoid poison baits, and knew what to do at once if by some mistake she should take one. She knew what guns are. She had learned to cut her morning and evening song very short. She had some acquaintance with dogs, enough to make her hate and distrust them all. But, above all, she had this idea: whenever danger is near, the very best move possible is to lay low, be very quiet, do nothing to attract notice. Perhaps the little brain that looked out of those changing yellow eyes was the storehouse of much other knowledge about men, but what it was did not appear.

The coyote was fully grown when the boss of the outfit bought a couple of thoroughbred greyhounds, wonderful runners, to see whether he could not entirely extirpate the remnant of the coyotes that still destroyed occasional sheep and calves on the range, and at the same time find amusement in the sport. He was tired of seeing that coyote in the yard; so, deciding to use her for training the dogs, he had her roughly thrown into a bag, then carried a quarter of a mile away and dumped out. At the same time the greyhounds were slipped and chivvied on. Away they went bounding at their matchless pace, that nothing else on four legs could equal, and away went the coyote, frightened by the noise of the men, frightened even to find herself free. Her quarter-mile start quickly shrank to one hundred yards, the one hundred to fifty, and on sped the flying dogs. Clearly there was no chance for her. On and nearer they came. In another minute she would have been stretched out—not a doubt of it. But on a sudden she stopped, turned and walked toward the dogs with her tail serenely waving in the air and a friendly cock to her ears.

Greyhounds are peculiar dogs. Anything that runs away they are going to catch and kill if they can. Anything that is calmly facing them becomes at once a non-combatant. They bounded over and past the coyote before they could curb their own impetuosity, and returned completely nonplussed. Possibly they recognized the coyote of the house yard as she stood there wagging her tail. The ranchmen were nonplussed too. Everyone was utterly taken aback, had a sense of failure, and the real victor in the situation was felt to be the audacious little coyote.

The greyhounds refused to attack an animal that wagged its tail and would not run; and the men, on seeing that the coyote could *walk* far enough away to avoid being caught by hand, took their ropes (lassos) and soon made her a prisoner once more.

The next day they decided to try again, but this time they added the white bull-terrier to the chasers. The coyote did as before. The greyhounds declined to be party to any attack on such a mild and friendly acquaintance. But the bull-terrier, who came puffing and panting on the scene three minutes later, had no such scruples. He was not so tall, but he was heavier than the coyote and, seizing her by her wool-protected neck, he shook her till, in a surprisingly short time, she lay limp and lifeless, at which all the men seemed pleased, and congratulated the terrier, while the greyhounds pottered around in restless perplexity.

A stranger in the party, a newly arrived Englishman, asked if he might have the brush—the tail, he explained—and on being told to help himself he picked up the victim by the tail, and with one awkward chop of his knife he cut it off at the middle, and the coyote dropped, but gave a shrill yelp of pain. She was not dead, only playing possum, and now she leaped up and vanished into a nearby thicket of cactus and sage.

With greyhounds a running animal is the signal for a run, so the two long-legged dogs and the white broad-chested dog dashed after the coyote. But right across their path, by

happy chance, there flashed a brown streak ridden by a snowy powder-puff, the visible but evanescent sign for Cottontail Rabbit. The coyote was not in sight now. The rabbit was, so the greyhounds dashed after the Cottontail, who took advantage of a prairie-dog's hole to seek safety in the bosom of Mother Earth, and the coyote made good her escape.

She had been a good deal jarred by the rude treatment of the terrier, and her mutilated tail gave her some pain. But otherwise she was all right, and she loped lightly away, keeping out of sight in the hollows, and so escaped among the fantastic buttes of the Badlands, to be eventually the founder of a new life among the coyotes of the Little Missouri.

Moses was preserved by the Egyptians till he had outlived the dangerous period, and learned from them wisdom enough to be the saviour of his people against those same Egyptians. So the bobtailed coyote was not only saved by man and carried over the dangerous period of puppyhood: she was also unwittingly taught by him how to baffle the traps, poisons, lassos, guns and dogs that had so long waged a war of extermination against her race.

III

THUS Tito escaped from man, and for the first time found herself face to face with the whole problem of life; for now she had her own living to get.

A wild animal has three sources of wisdom:

First, *the experience of its ancestors*, in the form of instinct, which is inborn learning, hammered into the race by ages of selection and tribulation. This is the most important to begin with, because it guards him from the moment he is born.

Second, *the experience of his parents and comrades*, learned chiefly by example. This becomes most important as soon as the young can run.

Third, *the personal experience* of the animal itself. This grows in importance as the animal ages.

The weakness of the first is its fixity; it cannot change to meet quickly changing conditions. The weakness of the second is the animal's inability freely to exchange ideas by language. The weakness of the third is the danger in acquiring it. But the three together are a strong arch.

Now Tito was in a new case. Perhaps never before had a coyote faced life with unusual advantages in the third kind of knowledge, none at all in the second, and with the first dormant. She travelled rapidly away from the ranchmen, keeping out of sight, and sitting down once in a while to lick her wounded tail stump. She came at last to a prairie-dog town. Many of the inhabitants were out, and they barked at the intruder, but all dodged down as soon as she came near. Her instinct taught her to try and catch one, but she ran about in vain for some time and then gave it up. She would have gone hungry that night, but that she found a couple of mice in the long grass by the river. Her mother had not taught her to hunt, but her instinct did, and the accident that she had an unusual brain made her profit very quickly by her experience.

In the days that followed she quickly learned how to

make a living; for mice, ground squirrels, prairie-dogs, rabbits and lizards were abundant, and many of these could be captured in open chase. But open chase, and sneaking as near as possible before beginning the open chase, lead naturally to stalking for a final spring. And before the moon had changed the coyote had learned how to make a comfortable living.

Once or twice she saw the men with the greyhounds coming her way. Most coyotes would perhaps have barked in bravado, or would have gone up to some high place whence they could watch the enemy; but Tito did no such foolish thing. Had she run, her moving form would have caught the eyes of the dogs, and then nothing could have saved her. She dropped where she was, and lay flat until the danger had passed. Thus her ranch training to lay low began to stand her in good stead, and so it came about that her weakness was her strength. The coyote kind had so long been famous for their speed, had so long learned to trust in their legs, that they never dreamed of a creature that could run them down. They were accustomed to play with their pursuers, and so rarely bestirred themselves to run from greyhounds till it was too late. But Tito, brought up at the end of a chain, was a poor runner. She had no reason to trust her legs. She rather trusted her wits, and so lived.

During that summer she stayed about the Little Missouri, learning the tricks of small-game hunting that she should have learned before she shed her milk teeth, and gaining in strength and speed. She kept far away from all the ranches and always hid on seeing a man or a strange beast, and so passed the summer alone. During the daytime she was not lonely, but when the sun went down she would feel the impulse to sing that wild song of the West which means so much to the coyotes.

It is not the invention of an individual nor of the present, but was slowly built out of the feelings of all coyotes in all ages. It expresses their nature and the plains that made their nature. When one begins it, it takes hold of the rest, as the fife and drum do with soldiers, or the ki-yi war-song with Indian braves. They respond to it as a bell-glass does to a certain note the moment that note is struck, ignoring other sounds. So the coyote, no matter how brought up, must vibrate at the night song of the plains, for it touches something in himself.

They sing it after sundown, when it becomes the rallying cry of their race and the friendly call to a neighbour; and they sing it as one boy in the woods halloas to another to say, 'All's well! Here am I. Where are you?' A form of it they sing to the rising moon, for this is the time for good hunting to begin. They sing when they see the new camp fire, for the same reason that a dog barks at a stranger. Yet another weird chant they have for the dawning before they steal quietly away from the offing of the camp—a wild weird squalling refrain,

'Wow-wow-wow-wow-wow-w-o-o-o-o-o-o-w',

again and again; and doubtless with many another change that man cannot distinguish any more than the coyote can distinguish the words in the cowboy's anathemas.

Tito instinctively uttered her music at the proper times. But sad experiences had taught her to cut it short and keep it low. Once or twice she had got a faraway reply from one of her own race, whereupon she had quickly ceased and timidly quit the neighbourhood.

One day, when on the Upper Garner's Creek, she found the trail where a piece of meat had been dragged along. It was a singularly inviting odour, and she followed it, partly out of curiosity. Presently she came on a piece of the meat itself. She was hungry; she was always hungry now. It was tempting, and although it had a peculiar odour, she swallowed it. Within a few minutes she felt a terrific pain. The memory of the poisoned meat the boy had given her was fresh. With trembling, foaming jaws she seized some blades of grass, and her stomach threw off the meat; but she fell in convulsions on the ground.

The trail of meat dragged along and the poison baits had been laid the day before by Wolver Jake. This morning he was riding the drag, and on coming up from the draw he saw, far ahead, the coyote struggling. He knew of course that it was poisoned, and rode quickly up; but the convulsions passed as he neared. By a mighty effort, at the sound of the horse's hoofs the coyote arose to her front feet. Jake drew his revolver and fired, but the only effect was fully to alarm her. She tried to run, but her hind legs were paralysed. She put forth all her strength, dragging her hind legs. Now, when the poison was no longer in the stomach, will-power could do a great deal. Had she been allowed to lie down then she would have been dead in five minutes; but the revolver shots and the man coming stirred her to strenuous action. Madly she struggled again and again to get her hind legs to work. All the force of desperate intent she brought to bear. It was like putting forth tenfold power to force the nervous fluids through their blocked-up channels as she dragged herself with marvellous speed downhill. What is nerve but will? The dead wires of her legs were hot with this fresh power, multiplied, injected, blasted into them. They had to give in. She felt them thrill with life again. Each wild shot from the gun lent vital help. Another fierce attempt, and one hind leg obeyed the call to duty. A few more bounds, and the other too fell in. Then lightly she loped away among the broken buttes, defying the agonizing gripe that still kept on inside.

Had Jake held off then she would yet have laid down and died; but he followed, and fired and fired, till in another mile she bounded free from pain, saved from her enemy by himself. He had compelled her to take the only cure, so she escaped.

And these were the ideas that she harvested that day: that curious smell on the meat stands for mortal agony. Let it alone! And she never forgot it; thenceforth she knew strychnine.

Fortunately dogs, traps and strychnine do not wage war

at once, for the dogs are as apt to be caught or poisoned as the coyotes. Had there been a single dog in the hunt that day Tito's history would have ended.

IV

When the weather grew cooler toward the end of autumn Tito had gone far toward repairing the defects in her early training. She was more like an ordinary coyote in her habits now, and she was more disposed to sing the sundown song.

One night, when she got a response, she yielded to the impulse again to call, and soon afterward a large dark coyote appeared. The fact that he was there at all was a guarantee of unusual gifts, for the war against his race was waged relentlessly by the cattlemen. He approached with caution. Tito's mane bristled with mixed feelings at the sight of one of her own kind. She crouched flat on the ground and waited. The newcomer came stiffly forward, nosing the wind; then up the wind nearly to her. Then he walked around so that she should wind him and, raising his tail, gently waved it. The first acts meant armed neutrality, but the last was a distinctly friendly signal. Then he approached, and she rose up suddenly and stood as high as she could to be smelled. Then she wagged the stump of her tail, and they considered themselves acquainted.

The newcomer was a very large coyote, half as tall again as Tito, and the dark patch on his shoulders was so large and black that the cowboys, when they came to know him, called him Saddleback. From that time these two continued more or less together. They were not always close together, often were miles apart during the day, but toward night one or the other would get on some high, open place and sing the loud

'Yap-yap-yap-yow-wow-wow-wow-wow',

and they would forgather for some foray on hand.

The physical advantages were with Saddleback, but the greater cunning was Tito's, so that she in time became the leader. Before a month a third coyote had appeared on the scene and become also a member of this loose-bound fraternity; and later two more appeared. Nothing succeeds like success. The little bobtailed coyote had had rare advantages of training just where the others were lacking: she knew the devices of man. She could not tell about these in words, but she could by the aid of a few signs and a great deal of example. It soon became evident that her methods of hunting were successful, whereas, when they went without her, they often had hard luck. A man at Boxelder Ranch had twenty sheep. The rules of the county did not allow anyone to own more, as this was a cattle range. The sheep were guarded by a large and fierce collie. One day in winter two of the coyotes tried to raid this flock by a bold dash, and all they got was a mauling from the collie. A few days later the band returned at dusk. Just how Tito arranged it, man cannot tell. We can only guess how she taught them their parts, but we know that she surely did. The coyotes hid in the willows. Then Saddleback, the bold and swift, walked openly toward the sheep and barked a loud defiance. The collie jumped up with bristling mane and furious growl, then, seeing the foe, dashed straight at him. Now was the time for the steady nerve and the unfailing limbs. Saddleback let the dog come near enough *almost* to catch him, and so beguiled him far and away into the woods, while the other coyotes, led by Tito, stampeded the sheep in twenty directions; then, following the farthest, they killed several and left them in the snow.

In the gloom of descending night the dog and his master laboured till they had gathered the bleating survivors; but next morning they found that four had been driven far away and killed, and the coyotes had had a banquet royal.

The shepherd poisoned the carcasses

and left them. Next night the coyotes returned. Tito sniffed the now frozen meat, detected the poison, gave a warning growl and scattered filth over the meat so that none of the band should touch it. One, however, who was fast and foolish, persisted in feeding in spite of Tito's warning, and when they came away he was lying poisoned and dead in the snow.

V

JAKE now heard on all sides that the coyotes were getting worse. So he set to work with many traps and much poison to destroy those on the Garner's Creek, and every little while he would go with the hounds and scour the Little Missouri south and east of the Chimney-pot Ranch; for it was understood that he must never run the dogs in country where traps and poison were laid. He worked in his erratic way all winter, and certainly did have some success. He killed a couple of grey wolves, said to be the last of their race, and several coyotes, some of which, no doubt, were of the bobtailed pack, which thereby lost those members which were lacking in wisdom.

Yet that winter was marked by a series of coyote raids and exploits; and usually the track in the snow or the testimony of eyewitnesses told that the master spirit of it all was a little bobtailed coyote.

One of these adventures was the cause of much talk. The coyote challenge sounded close to the Chimney-pot Ranch after sundown. A dozen dogs responded with the usual clamour. But only the bull-terrier dashed away toward the place whence the coyotes had called, for the reason that he was loose. His chase was fruitless and he came back growling. Twenty minutes later there was another coyote yell close at hand. Off dashed the terrier as before. In a minute his excited yapping told that he had sighted his game and was in full chase. Away he went, furiously barking, until his voice was lost afar, and never more was heard. In the morning the men read in the snow the tale of the night. The first cry of the coyotes was to find out if all the dogs were loose; then, having found that only one was free, they laid a plan. Five coyotes hid along the side of the trail; one went forward and called till it had decoyed the rash terrier, and then led him right into the ambush. What chance had he with six? They tore him limb from limb and devoured him too, at the very spot where once he had worried Coyotito. And next morning, when the men came, they saw by the signs that the whole thing had been planned, and that the leader whose cunning had made it a success was a little bobtailed coyote.

The men were angry, and Lincoln was furious; but Jake remarked: 'Well, I guess that bobtail came back and got even with that terrier.'

VI

When spring was near, the annual love season of the coyotes came on. Saddleback and Tito had been together merely as companions all winter, but now a new feeling was born. There was not much courting. Saddleback simply showed his teeth to possible rivals. There was no ceremony. They had been friends for months and now, in the light of the new feeling, they naturally took to each other and were mated. Coyotes do not give each other names as do mankind, but have one sound like a growl and short howl, which stands for 'mate' or 'husband' or 'wife'. This they use in calling to each other, and it is by recognizing the tone of the voice that they know who is calling.

The loose rambling brotherhood of the coyotes was broken up now, for the others also paired off and, since the returning warm weather was bringing out the prairie-dogs and small game, there was less need to combine for hunting. Ordinarily coyotes do not sleep in dens or in any fixed place. They move about all night while it is cool, then during the daytime they get a few hours' sleep in the sun, on some quiet hillside that also gives a chance to watch out. But the mating season changes this habit somewhat.

As the weather grew warm Tito and Saddleback set about preparing a den for the expected family. In a warm little hollow, an old badger abode was cleaned out, enlarged and deepened. A quantity of leaves and grass was carried into it and arranged in a comfortable nest. The place selected for it was a dry sunny nook among the hills, half a mile west of the Little Missouri. Thirty yards from it was a ridge which commanded a wide view of the grassy slopes and cottonwood groves by the river. Men would have called the spot very beautiful, but it is tolerably certain that that side of it never touched the coyotes at all.

Tito began to be much preoccupied with her impending duties. She stayed quietly in the neighbourhood of the den, and lived on such food as Saddleback brought her, or she herself could easily catch, and also on the little stores that she had buried at other times. She knew every prairie-dog town in the region, as well as all the best places for mice and rabbits.

Not far from the den was the very dog town that first she had crossed the day she had gained her liberty and lost her tail. If she were capable of such retrospect, she must have laughed to herself to think what a fool she was then. The change in her methods was now shown. Somewhat removed from the others, a prairie-dog had made his den in the most approved style, and now when Tito peered over he was feeding on the grass ten yards from his own door. A prairie-dog away from the others is of course easier to catch than one in the middle of the town, for he has but one pair of eyes to guard him; so Tito set about stalking this one. How was she to do it when there was no cover, nothing but short grass and a few low weeds? The white bear knows how to approach the seal on the flat ice, and the Indian how to get within striking distance of the grazing deer. Tito knew how to do the same trick, and although one of the town owls flew over with a warning chuckle, Tito set about her plan. A prairie-dog cannot see well unless he is sitting up on his hind legs; his eyes are of little use when he is nosing in the grass; and Tito knew this. Further, a yellowish-grey animal on a yellowish-grey landscape is invisible till it moves. Tito seemed to know that. So, without any attempt to crawl or hide, she walked gently upwind toward the prairie-dog. Upwind, not in order to prevent the prairie-dog smelling her, but so that she could smell him, which came to the same thing. As soon as the prairie-dog sat up with some food in his hand she froze into a statue. As soon as he dropped again to nose the grass, she walked steadily nearer, watching his every move so that she might be motionless each time he sat up to see what his distant brothers were barking at. Once or twice he seemed alarmed by the calls of his friends, but he saw nothing and resumed his feeding. She soon cut the fifty yards down to ten, and the ten to five and still was undiscovered. Then, when again the prairie-dog dropped down to seek more fodder, she made a quick dash and bore him off kicking and squealing. Thus does the angel of the pruning-knife lop off those that are heedless and foolishly indifferent to the advantage of society.

VII

TITO had many adventures in which she did not come out so well. Once she nearly caught an antelope fawn, but the hunt was spoiled by the sudden appearance of the mother, who gave Tito a stinging blow on the side of the head and ended her hunt for that day. She never again made that mistake—she had sense. Once or twice she had to jump to escape the strike of a rattlesnake. Several times she had been fired at by hunters with long-range rifles. And more and more she had to look out for the terrible grey wolves. The grey wolf, of course, is much larger and stronger than the coyote, but the coyote has the advantage of speed and can always escape in the open. All it must beware of is being caught in a corner. Usually when a grey wolf howls the coyotes go quietly about their business elsewhere.

Tito had a curious fad occasionally seen among the wolves and coyotes, of carrying in her mouth, for miles, such things as seemed to be interesting and yet were not tempting as eatables. Many a time had she trotted a mile or two with an old buffalo horn or a cast-off shoe, only to drop it when something else attracted her attention. The cowboys who remark these things have various odd explanations to offer: one, that it is done to stretch the jaws, or keep them in practice, just as a man in training carries weights. Coyotes have, in common with dogs and wolves, the habit of calling at certain stations along their line of travel, to leave a record of their visit. These stations may be a stone, a tree, a post or an old buffalo skull, and the coyote calling there can learn, by the odour and track of the last comer, just who the caller was, whence he came and whither he went. The whole country is marked out by these intelligence depots. Now it often happens that a coyote that has not much else to do will carry a dry bone or some other useless object in its mouth, but, sighting the signal-post, will go toward it to get the news, lay down the bone, and afterward forget to take it along, so that the signal-posts in time become further marked with a curious collection of odds and ends.

This singular habit was the cause of a disaster to the Chimney-pot wolfhounds and a corresponding advantage to the coyotes in the war. Jake had laid a line of poison baits on the western bluffs. Tito knew what they were and spurned them as usual; but, finding more later, she gathered up three or four and crossed the Little Missouri toward the ranch house. This she circled at a safe distance; but when something made the pack of dogs break out into clamour, Tito dropped the baits, and next day, when the dogs were taken out for exercise, they found and devoured these scraps of meat, so that in ten minutes there were four hundred dollars' worth of greyhounds lying dead. This led to an edict against poisoning in that district, and thus was a great boon to the coyotes.

Tito quickly learned that not only each kind of game must be hunted in a special way, but different ones of each kind may require quite different treatment. The prairie-dog with the outlying den was really an easy prey, but the town was quite compact now that he was gone. Near the centre of it was a fine big fat prairie-dog, a perfect alderman, that she had made several vain attempts to capture. On one occasion she had crawled almost within leaping distance, when the angry *bizz* of a rattlesnake just ahead warned her that she was in danger. Not that the rattler cared anything about the prairie-dog, but he did not wish to be disturbed;

and Tito, who had an instinctive fear of the snake, was forced to abandon the hunt. The open stalk proved an utter failure with the alderman, for the situation of his den made every dog in the town his sentinel; but he was too good to lose, and Tito waited until circumstances made a new plan.

All coyotes have a trick of watching from a high lookout whatever passes along the roads. After it has passed they go down and examine its track. Tito had this habit, except that she was always careful to keep out of sight herself.

One day a wagon passed from the town to the southward. Tito lay low and watched it. Something dropped on the road. When the wagon was out of sight Tito sneaked down, first to smell the trail as a matter of habit, second to see what it was that had dropped. The object was really an apple, but Tito saw only an unattractive round green thing like a cactus leaf without spines, and of a peculiar smell. She snuffed it, spurned it and was about to pass on; but the sun shone on it so brightly, and it rolled so curiously when she pawed, that she picked it up in a mechanical way and trotted back over the rise, where she found herself at the dog town. Just then two great prairie hawks came skimming like pirates over the plain. As soon as they were in sight the prairie-dogs all barked, jerking their tails at each bark, and hid below. When all were gone Tito walked on toward the hole of the big fat fellow whose body she coveted and, dropping the apple on the ground a couple of feet from the rim of the crater that formed his home, she put her nose down to enjoy the delicious smell of dog fat. Even his den smelled more fragrant than those of the rest. Then she went quietly behind a greasewood bush, in a lower place some twenty yards away, and lay flat. After a few seconds some venturesome prairie-dog looked out and, seeing nothing, gave the 'all's well' bark. One by one they came out, and in twenty minutes the town was alive as before. One of the last to come out was the fat old alderman. He always took good care of his own precious self. He peered out cautiously a few times, then climbed to the top of his lookout. A prairie-dog hole is shaped like a funnel, going straight down. Around the top of this is built a high ridge which serves as a lookout, and also makes sure that, no matter how they may slip in their hurry, they are certain to drop into the funnel and be swallowed up by the all-protecting earth. On the outside the ground slopes away gently from the funnel. Now, when the alderman saw that strange round thing at his threshold he was afraid. Second inspection led him to believe that it was not dangerous, but was probably interesting. He went cautiously toward it, smelled it and tried to nibble it; but the apple rolled away, for it was round, and the ground was smooth as well as sloping. The prairie-dog followed and gave it a nip which satisfied him that the strange object would make good eating. But each time he nibbled it rolled farther away. The coast seemed clear, all the other prairie-dogs were out, so the fat alderman did not hesitate to follow up the dodging, shifting apple.

This way and that it wriggled, and he followed. Of course it worked toward the low place where grew the greasewood bush. The little tastes of apple that he got only whetted his appetite. The alderman was more and more interested. Foot by foot he was led from his hole toward that old, familiar bush, and had no thought of anything but the joy of eating. And Tito curled herself and braced her sinewy legs, and measured the distance between, until it dwindled to not more than three good jumps; then up and like an arrow she went, and grabbed and bore him off at last.

Now it will never be known whether it was accident or design that led to the placing of that apple, but it proved important, and if such a thing were to happen once or twice to a smart coyote—and it is usually clever ones that get such chances—it might easily grow into a new trick of hunting.

After a hearty meal Tito buried the rest in a cold place, not to get rid of it, but to hide it for future use; and a little later, when she was too weak to hunt much, her various hoards of this sort came in very useful. True, the meat had turned very strong; but Tito was not critical, and she had no fears or theories of microbes, so suffered no ill effects.

VIII

The lovely Hiawathan spring was touching all things in the fairy Badlands. Oh, why are they called Badlands? If Nature sat down deliberately on the eighth day of creation and said, 'Now work is done, let's play; let's make a place that shall combine everything that is finished and wonderful and beautiful—a paradise for man and bird and beast', it was surely then that she made these wild, fantastic hills, teeming with life, radiant with gayest flowers, varied with sylvan groves, bright with prairie sweeps and brimming lakes and streams. In foreground, offing and distant hills that change at every step, we find some proof that Nature squandered here the riches that in other lands she used as sparingly as gold, with colourful sky above and colourful land below, and the distance blocked by sculptured buttes that are built of precious stones and ores, and tinged as by a lasting and unspeakable sunset. And yet, for all this ten times gorgeous wonderland enchanted, blind man has found no better name than one which says, *The road to it is hard.*

The little hollow west of Chimney Butte was freshly grassed. The dangerous-looking Spanish bayonets, that through the bygone winter had waged war with all things, now sent out their contribution to the peaceful triumph of the spring, in flowers that have stirred even the chilly scientists to name them *Gloriosa*; and the cactus, poisonous, most reptilian of herbs, surprised the world with a splendid

bloom as little like itself as the pearl is like its mother shellfish. The sage and the greasewood lent their gold, and the sand-anemone tinged the Badland hills like bluish snow; and in the air and earth and hills on every hand was felt the fecund promise of the spring. This was the end of the winter famine, the beginning of the summer feast, and this was the time by the All-mother ordained when first the little coyotes should see the light of day.

A mother does not have to learn to love her helpless squirming brood. They bring the love with them—not much or little, not measurable, but perfect love. And in that dimly lighted warm abode she fondled them and licked them and cuddled them with heartful warmth and tenderness that was as much a new epoch in her life as in theirs.

But the pleasure of loving them was measured in the same measure as anxiety for their safety. In bygone days her care had been mainly for herself. All she had learned in her strange puppyhood, all she had picked up since, was bent to the main idea of self-preservation. Now she was ousted from her own affections by her brood. Her chief care was to keep their home concealed, and this was not very hard at first, for she left them only when she must, to supply her own wants.

She came and went with great care, and only after

spying well the land so that none should see and find the place of her treasure. If it were possible for the little ones' idea of their mother and the cowboys' idea to be set side by side they would be found to have nothing in common, though both were right in their point of view. The ranchmen knew the coyote only as a pair of despicable, cruel jaws, borne around on tireless legs, steered by incredible cunning and leaving behind a track of destruction. The little ones knew her as a loving, gentle, all-powerful guardian. For them her breast was soft and warm and infinitely tender. She fed and warmed them, she was their wise and watchful keeper. She was always at hand with food when they hungered, with wisdom to foil the cunning of their foes, and with a heart of courage tried to crown her well-laid plans for them with uniform success.

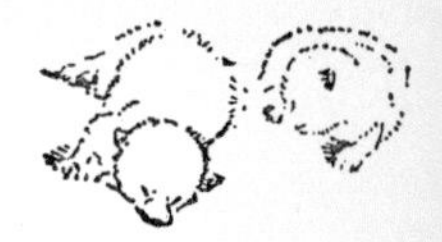

A baby coyote is a shapeless, senseless, wriggling and—to everyone but its mother—a most uninteresting little lump. But after its eyes are open, after it has developed its legs, after it has learned to play in the sun with its brothers, or run at the gentle call of its mother when she brings home game for it to feed on, the baby coyote becomes one of the cutest, dearest little rascals on earth. And when the nine that made up Coyotito's brood had reached this stage, it did not require the glamour of motherhood to make them objects of the greatest interest.

The summer was now on. The little ones were beginning to eat flesh-meat, and Tito, with some assistance from Saddleback, was kept busy to supply both themselves and the brood. Sometimes she brought them a prairie-dog, at other times she would come home with a whole bunch of gophers and mice in her jaws; and once or twice, by the clever trick of relay-chasing, she succeeded in getting one of the big northern jack-rabbits for the little folks at home.

After they had feasted they would lie around in the sun for a time, Tito would mount guard on a bank and scan the earth and air with her keen brassy eye, lest any dangerous foe should find their happy valley; and the merry pups played little games of tag, or chased the butterflies, or had apparently desperate encounters with each other, or tore and worried the bones and feathers than now lay about the threshold of the home. One, the least (for there is usually a runt), stayed near the mother and climbed on her back or pulled at her tail. They made a lovely picture as they played, and the wrestling group in the middle seemed the focus of it all at first; but a keener, later look would have rested on the mother, quiet, watchful, not without anxiety, but, above all, with a face full of motherly tenderness. Oh, she was so proud and happy, and she would sit there and watch them and silently love them till it was time to go home, or until some sign of distant danger showed. Then, with a low growl, she gave the signal, and all disappeared from sight in a twinkling, after which she would set off to meet and turn the danger, or go on a fresh hunt for food.

IX

Wolver Jake had several plans for making a fortune, but each in turn was abandoned as soon as he found that it meant work. At one time or other most men of this kind see the chance of their lives in a poultry farm. They cherish the idea that somehow the poultry do all the work. And without troubling himself about the details Jake devoted an unexpected windfall to the purchase of a dozen turkeys for his latest scheme. The turkeys were duly housed in one end of Jake's shanty, so as to be well guarded, and for a couple of days were the object of absorbing interest, and had the best of care—too much, really. But Jake's ardour waned about the third day; then the recurrent necessity for long celebrations at Medora, and the ancient allurements of idle hours spent lying on the tops of sunny buttes and of days spent sponging on the hospitality of distant ranches, swept away the last pretence of attention to his poultry farm. The turkeys were utterly neglected—left to forage for themselves; and each time that Jake returned to his uninviting shanty, after a few days' absence, he found fewer birds, till at last none but the old Gobbler was left.

Jake cared little about the loss, but was filled with indignation against the thief.

He was now installed as wolver to the Broad Arrow outfit. That is, he was supplied with poison, traps and horses, and was also entitled to all he could make out of wolf bounties. A reliable man would have got pay in addition, for the ranchmen are generous, but Jake was not reliable.

Every wolver knows of course that his business naturally drops into several well-marked periods.

In the late winter and early spring—the love season—the hounds will not hunt a she-wolf. They will quit the trail of a he-wolf at this time to take up that of a she-wolf, but when they do overtake her they, for some sentimental reason, invariably let her go in peace. In August and September the young coyotes and wolves are just beginning to run alone, and they are then easily trapped and poisoned. A month or so later the survivors have learned how to take care of themselves, but in the early summer the wolver knows that there are dens full of little ones all through the hills. Each den has from five to fifteen pups, and the only difficulty is to know the whereabouts of these family homes.

One way of finding the dens is to watch from some tall butte for a coyote carrying food to its brood. As this kind of wolving involved much lying still, it suited Jake very well. So, equipped with a Broad Arrow horse and the boss's field-glasses, he put in week after week at den-hunting—that is, lying asleep in some possible lookout, with an occasional glance over the country when it seemed easier to do that than to lie still.

The coyotes had learned to avoid the open. They generally went homeward along the sheltered hollows; but this was not always possible, and one day, while exercising his arduous profession in the country west of Chimney Butte, Jake's glasses and glance fell by chance on a dark spot which moved along an open hillside. It was grey, and it looked like this: and even Jake knew that that meant coyote. If it had been a grey wolf it would have been so: with tail up. A fox would have looked so: the large ears and tail and the yellow colour would have marked it. And a deer would have looked so: that dark shade from the front end meant something in his mouth, probably something being carried home—and that would mean a den of little ones.

He made careful note of the place, and returned there next day to watch, selecting a high butte near where he had seen the coyote carrying the food. But all day passed and he saw nothing. Next day, however, he descried a dark coyote, old Saddleback, carrying a large bird, and by the help of the glasses he made out that it was a turkey; and then he knew that the yard at home was quite empty, and he also knew where the rest of them had gone, and vowed terrible vengeance when he should find the den. He followed Saddleback with his eyes as far as possible, and that was no great way, then went to the place to see if he could track him any farther; but he found no guiding signs, and he did not chance on the little hollow that was the playground of Tito's brood.

Meanwhile Saddleback came to the little hollow and gave the low call that always conjured from the earth the unruly procession of the nine riotous little pups, and they dashed at the turkey and pulled and worried till it was torn up, and each that got a piece ran to one side alone and silently proceeded to eat, seizing his portion in his jaws when another came near, and growling his tiny growl as he showed the brownish whites of his eyes in his effort to watch the intruder. Those that got the softer parts to feed on were well fed. But the three that did not turned all their energies on the frame of the Gobbler, and over that there waged a battle royal. This way and that they tugged and tussled, getting off occasional scraps, but really hindering each other feeding, till Tito glided in and deftly cut the turkey into three or four, when each dashed off with a prize, over which he sat and chewed and smacked his lips and jammed his head down sideways to bring the backmost teeth to bear, while the baby runt scrambled into the home den, carrying in triumph his share—the Gobbler's grotesque head and neck.

X

JAKE felt that he had been grievously wronged, indeed ruined, by that coyote that stole his turkeys. He vowed he would skin them alive when he found the pups, and took pleasure in thinking about how he would do it. His attempt to follow Saddleback by trailing was a failure, and all his searching for the den was useless, but he had come prepared for any emergency. In case he found the den he had brought a pick and shovel; in case he did not he had brought a living white hen.

The hen he now took to a broad open place near where he had seen Saddleback, and there he tethered her to a stick of wood that she could barely drag. Then he made himself comfortable on a lookout that was near, and lay still to watch. The hen of course ran to the end of the string, and then lay on the ground flopping stupidly. Presently the clog gave enough to ease the strain; she turned by mere chance in another direction, and so, for a time, stood up to look around.

The day went slowly by, and Jake lazily stretched himself on the blanket in his spying-place. Towards evening Tito came by on a hunt. This was not surprising, for the den was only half a mile away. Tito had learned, among other rules, this: 'Never show yourself on the sky-line.' In former days the coyotes used to trot along the tops of the ridges for the sake of the chance to watch both sides. But men and guns had taught Tito that in this way you are sure to be seen. She therefore made a practice of running along near the top, and once in a while peeping over.

This was what she did that evening as she went out to hunt for the children's supper, and her keen eyes fell on the white hen, stupidly stalking about and turning up its eyes in a wise way each time a harmless turkey-buzzard came in sight against a huge white cloud.

Tito was puzzled. This was something new. It *looked* like game, but she feared to take any chances. She circled all around without showing herself, then decided that, whatever it might be, it was better let alone. As she passed on, a faint whiff of smoke caught her attention. She followed cautiously and under a butte far from the hen she found Jake's camp. His bed was there, his horse was picketed, and on the remains of the fire was a pot which gave out a smell which she well knew about men's camps—the smell of coffee. Tito felt uneasy at this proof that a man was staying so near her home, but she went off quietly on her hunt, keeping out of sight, and Jake knew nothing of her visit.

About sundown he took in his decoy hen, as owls were abundant, and went back to his camp.

XI

NEXT day the hen was again put out, and late that afternoon Saddleback came trotting by. As soon as his eye fell on the white hen he stopped short, his head on one side, and gazed. Then he circled to get the wind, and went cautiously sneaking nearer, very cautiously, somewhat puzzled, till he got a whiff that reminded him of the place where he had found those turkeys. The hen took alarm and tried to run away; but Saddleback made a rush, seized the hen so fiercely that the string was broken and away he dashed toward the home valley.

Jake had fallen asleep, but the squawk of the hen happened to awaken him and he sat up in time to see her borne away in old Saddleback's jaws.

As soon as they were out of sight Jake took up the white-feather trail. At first it was easily followed, for the hen had shed plenty of plumes in her struggles; but once she was dead in Saddleback's jaws very few feathers were dropped except where she was carried through the brush. But Jake was following quietly and certainly, for Saddleback had gone nearly in a straight line home to the little ones with the dangerous telltale prize. Once or twice there was a puzzling delay when the coyote had changed his course or gone over an open place; but one white feather was good for fifty yards and, when the daylight was gone, Jake was not two hundred yards from the hollow, in which at that very moment were the nine little pups, having a perfectly delightful time with the hen, pulling it to pieces, feasting and growling, sneezing the white feathers from their noses or coughing them from their throats.

If a puff of wind had now blown from them toward Jake, it might have carried a flurry of snowy plumes or even the merry cries of the little revellers, and the den would have been discovered at once. But, as luck would have it, the evening lull was on, and all distant sounds were hidden by the crashing that Jake made in trying to trace his feather guides through the last thicket.

About this time Tito was returning home with a magpie that she had captured by watching till it went to feed within the ribs of a dead horse, when she ran across Jake's trail. Now, a man on foot is always a suspicious character in this country. She followed the trail for a little to see where he was going, and that she knew at once from the scent. How it tells her no one can say, yet all hunters know that it does. And Tito marked that it was going straight toward her home. Thrilled with new fear, she hid the bird she was carrying, then followed the trail of the man. Within a few minutes she could hear him in the thicket, and Tito realized the terrible danger that was threatening. She went swiftly, quietly around to the den hollow, came on the heedless little

roisterers, after giving the signal call, which prevented them taking alarm at her approach; but she must have had a shock when she saw how marked the hollow and the den were now, all drifted over with feathers white as snow. Then she gave the danger call that sent them all to earth, and the little glade was still.

Her own nose was so thoroughly and always her guide that it was not likely she thought of the white feathers being the telltale. But now she realized that a man, one she knew of old as a treacherous character, one whose scent had always meant mischief to her, that had been associated with all her own troubles and the cause of nearly all her desperate danger, was close to her darlings; was tracking them down; in a few minutes would surely have them in his merciless power.

Oh, the wrench to the mother's heart at the thought of what she could foresee! But the warmth of the mother love lent life to the mother wit. Having sent the little ones out of sight, and by a sign conveyed to Saddleback her alarm, she swiftly came back to the man, then she crossed before him, thinking in her half-reasoning way, that the man *must* be following a foot scent just as she herself would do, but would of course take the stronger line of tracks she was now laying. She did not realize that the failing daylight made any difference. Then she trotted to one side and, to make doubly sure of being followed, she uttered the fiercest challenge she could, just as many a time she had done to make the dogs pursue her:

'Grrr-wow-wow-wa-a-a-a-h,'

and stood still; then ran a little nearer and did it again, and then again much nearer, and repeated her bark, so determined was she that the wolver should follow her.

Of course the wolver could see nothing of the coyote,

for the shades were falling. He had to give up the hunt anyway. His understanding of the details was as different as possible from that the mother coyote had, and yet it came to the same thing. He recognized that the coyote's bark was the voice of the distressed mother trying to call him away. So he knew the brood must be close at hand, and all he now had to do was return in the morning and complete his search. So he made his way back to his camp.

XII

SADDLEBACK thought they had won the victory. He felt secure, because the foot scent that he might have supposed the man to be following would be stale by morning. Tito did not feel so safe. That two-legged beast was close to her home and her little ones; had barely been turned aside; might come back yet.

The wolver watered and repicketed his horse, kindled the fire anew, made his coffee and ate his evening meal, then smoked awhile before lying down to sleep, thinking occasionally of the little woolly scalps he expected to gather in the morning.

He was about to roll up in his blanket when, out of the dark distance, there sounded the evening cry of the coyote, the rolling challenge of more than one voice. Jake grinned in fiendish glee, and said: 'There you are all right. Howl some more. I'll see you in the morning.'

It was the ordinary, or rather *one* of the ordinary, camp calls of the coyote. It was sounded once, and then all was still. Jake soon forgot it in his loggish slumber.

The callers were Tito and Saddleback. The challenge was not an empty bluff. It had a distinct purpose behind it—to know for sure whether the enemy had any dogs with him; and because there was no responsive bark Tito knew that he had none.

Then Tito waited for an hour or so till the flickering fire had gone dead, and the only sound of life about the camp

was the cropping of the grass by the picketed horse. Tito crept near softly, so softly that the horse did not see her till she was within twenty feet; then he gave a start that swung the tightened picket-rope up into the air, and snorted gently. Tito went quietly forward, and opening her wide gape, took the rope in, almost under her ears, between the great scissor-like back teeth, then chewed it for a few seconds. The fibres quickly frayed, and, aided by the strain the nervous horse still kept up, the last of the strands gave way, and the horse was free. He was not much alarmed —he knew the smell of coyote—and after jumping three steps and walking six he stopped.

The sounding thumps of his hoofs on the ground awoke the sleeper. He looked up, but, seeing the horse standing there, he went calmly off to sleep again, supposing that all went well.

Tito had sneaked away, but she now returned like a shadow, avoided the sleeper, but came around, sniffed doubtfully at the coffee, and then puzzled over a tin can, while Saddleback examined the frying-pan full of 'camp-sinkers' and then defiled both cakes and pan with dirt. The bridle hung on a low bush; the coyotes did not know what it was, but just for luck they cut it into several pieces, then, taking the sacks that held Jake's bacon and flour, they carried them far away and buried them in the sand.

Having done all the mischief she could, Tito, followed by her mate, now set off for a wooded gully some miles away, where was a hole that had been made first by a chipmunk, but enlarged by several other animals, including a fox that had tried to dig out its occupants. Tito stopped and looked at many possible places before she settled on this. Then she set to work to dig. Saddleback had followed in a half-comprehending way, till he saw what she was doing. Then when she, tired with digging, came out, he went into the hole, and after snuffing about went on with the work, throwing out the earth between his hind legs; and when it was piled up behind he would come out and push it yet farther away.

And so they worked for hours, not a word said, and yet with a sufficient comprehension of the object in view to work in relief of each other. And by the time the morning came they had a den big enough to do for their home, in case they must move, though it would not compare with the one in the grassy hollow.

XIII

It was nearly sunrise before the wolver awoke. With the true instinct of a plainsman he turned to look for the horse. *It was gone.* What his ship is to the sailor, what wings are to the bird, what money is to the merchant, the horse is to the plainsman. Without it he is helpless, lost at sea, wing broken, crippled in business. Afoot on the plains is the sum of earthly terrors. Even Jake realized this, and ere his foggy wits had fully felt the shock he sighted the steed afar on a flat, grazing and stepping ever farther from the camp. At a second glance Jake noticed that the horse was trailing the rope. If the rope had been left behind Jake would have known that it was hopeless to try to catch him; he would have finished his den-hunt and found the little coyotes. But with the trailing rope there was a good chance of catching the horse; so Jake set out to try.

Of all maddening things there is nothing worse than to be almost, but not quite, able to catch your horse. Do what he might, Jake could not get quite near enough to seize that short rope, and the horse led him on and on until at last they were well on the homeward trail.

Now Jake was afoot anyhow, so seeing no better plan he set out to follow that horse right back to the ranch.

But when about seven miles were covered Jake succeeded in catching him. He rigged up a rough *jaquima* with the rope and rode barebacked in fifteen minutes over the three miles

that lay between him and the sheep ranch, giving vent all the way to his pent-up feelings in cruel abuse of that horse. Of course it did not do any good, and he knew that, but he considered it was heaps of satisfaction.

Here Jake got a meal and borrowed a saddle and a mongrel hound that could run a trail, and returned late in the afternoon to finish his den-hunt. Had he known it, he now could have found it without the aid of the cur, for it was really close at hand when he took up the feather trail where last he had left it. Within one hundred yards he rose to the top of the little ridge; then just over it, almost face to face, he came on a coyote, carrying in its mouth a large rabbit. The coyote leaped just at the same moment that Jake fired his revolver, and the dog broke into a fierce yelling and dashed off in pursuit, while Jake blazed and blazed away, without effect, and wondered why the coyote should still hang on to that rabbit as she ran for her life with the dog yelling at her heels. Jake followed as far as he could and fired at each chance, but scored no hit. So when they had vanished among the buttes he left the dog to follow or come back as he pleased, while he returned to the den, which of course was plain enough now. Jake knew that the pups were there yet. Had he not seen the mother bringing a rabbit for them?

So he set to work with pick and shovel all the rest of that day. There were plenty of signs that the den had inhabitants and, duly encouraged, he dug on, and after several hours of the hardest work he had ever done he came to the end of the den—*only to find it empty*. After cursing his luck at the first shock of disgust, he put on his strong leather glove and groped about in the nest. He felt something firm and drew it out. It was the head and neck of his own turkey Gobbler, and that was all he got for his pains.

XIV

Tito had not been idle during the time that the enemy was horse-hunting. Whatever Saddleback might have done, Tito would live in no fool's paradise. Having finished the new den, she trotted back to the little valley of feathers, and the first young one that came to meet her at the door of this home was a broad-headed one much like herself. She seized him by the neck and set off, carrying him across country toward the new den, a couple of miles away. Every little while she had to put her offspring down to rest and give it a chance to breathe. This made the moving slow, and the labour of transporting the pups occupied all that day, for Saddleback was not allowed to carry any of them, probably because he was too rough.

Beginning with the biggest and brightest, they were carried away one at a time, and late in the afternoon only the runt was left. Tito had not only worked at digging all night, she had also trotted over thirty miles, half of it with a heavy baby to carry. But she did not rest. She was just coming out of the den, carrying her youngest in her mouth, when over the very edge of this hollow appeared the mongrel hound, and a little way behind him Wolver Jake.

Away went Tito, holding the baby tight, and away went the dog behind her.

Bang! Bang! Bang! said the revolver.

But not a shot touched her. Then over the ridge they dashed, where the revolver could not reach her, and sped across a flat, the tired coyote and her baby, and the big fierce hound behind her, bounding his hardest. Had she been fresh and unweighted she could soon have left the clumsy cur that now was barking furiously on her track and rather gaining than losing in the race. But she put forth all her strength, careered along a slope, where she gained a little, then down across a brushy flat where the cruel bushes robbed her of all she had gained. But again into the open they came, and the wolver, labouring far behind, got sight of them and fired again and again with his revolver, and only stirred the dust, but still it made her dodge and lose time, and it also spurred the dog. The hunter saw the coyote, his old acquaintance of the bobtail, carrying still, as he thought, the jack-rabbit she had been bringing to her brood, and wondered at her strange persistence. 'Why doesn't she drop that weight when flying for her life?' But on she went and gamely bore her load over the hills, the man cursing his luck that he had not brought his horse, and the mongrel bounding in deadly earnest but thirty feet behind her. Then suddenly in front of Tito yawned a little cut-bank gully. Tired and weighted, she dared not try the leap; she skirted around. But the dog was fresh; he cleared it easily, and the mother's start was cut down by half. But on she went, straining to hold the little one high above the scratching brush and the dangerous bayonet spikes; but straining too much, for the helpless cub was choking in his mother's grip. She must lay him down or strangle him; with such a weight she could not much longer keep out of reach. She tried to give the howl for help, but her voice was muffled by the cub, now struggling for breath, and as she tried to ease her grip on him a sudden wrench jerked him from her mouth into the grass—into the power of the merciless hound. Tito was far smaller than the dog; ordinarily she would have held him in fear; but her little one, her baby, was the only thought now, and as the brute sprang forward to tear it in his wicked jaws she leaped between and stood facing him with all her mane erect, her teeth exposed, and plainly showed her resolve to save her young one at any price. The dog was not brave, only confident that he was bigger and had the man behind him. But the man was far away and, balked in his first rush at the trembling little coyote that tried to hide in the grass, the cur hesitated a moment, and Tito howled the long howl for help—the muster call:

'Yap-yap-yap-yah-yah-yah-h-h-h-h
Yap-yap-yap-yah-yah-yah-h-h-h-h,'

and made the buttes around re-echo so that Jake could not

tell where it came from; but someone else there was that heard and *did* know whence it came. The dog's courage revived on hearing something like a faraway shout. Again he sprang at the little one, but again the mother balked him with her own body, and then they closed in deadly struggle. 'Oh, if Saddleback would only come!' But no one came, and now she had no further chance to call. Weight is everything in a closing fight, and Tito soon went down, bravely fighting to the last, but clearly worsted; and the hound's courage grew with the sight of victory, and all he thought of now was to finish her and then kill her helpless baby in its turn. He had no ears or eyes for any other thing, till out of the nearest sage there flashed a streak of grey, and in a trice the big-voiced coward was hurled back by a foe almost as heavy as himself—hurled back with a crippled shoulder. Dash, chop, and staunch old Saddleback sprang on him again. Tito struggled to her feet, and they closed on him together. His courage fled at once when he saw the odds, and all he wanted now was safe escape—escape from Saddleback, whose speed was like the wind, escape from Tito, whose baby's life was at stake. Not twenty jumps away did he get; not breath enough had he to howl for help to his master in the distant hills; not fifteen yards away from her little one that he meant to tear, they tore him all to bits.

And Tito lifted the rescued young one, and travelling as slowly as she wished, they reached the new-made den. There the family safely reunited, far away from danger of further attack by Wolver Jake or his kind.

And there they lived in peace till their mother had finished their training, and every one of them grew up wise in the ancient learning of the plains, wise in the later wisdom that the ranchers' war has forced upon them, and not only they, but their children's children, too.

The buffalo herds have gone; they have succumbed to the rifles of the hunters. The antelope droves are nearly gone; hound and lead were too much for them. The black-tail bands have dwindled before axe and fence. The ancient dwellers of the Badlands have faded like snow under the new conditions, but the coyotes are no more in fear of extinction. Their morning and evening song still sounds from the level buttes, as it did long years ago when every plain was a teeming land of game. They have learned the deadly secrets of traps and poisons, they know how to baffle the gunner and hound, they have matched their wits with the hunter's wits. They have learned how to prosper in a land of man-made plenty, in spite of the worst that man can do, and it was Tito that taught them how.

Lobo

The King of Currumpaw

I

CURRUMPAW is a vast cattle range in northern New Mexico. It is a land of rich pastures and teeming flocks and herds, a land of rolling mesas and precious running waters that at length unite in the Currumpaw River, from which the whole region is named. And the king whose despotic power was felt over its entire extent was an old grey wolf.

Old Lobo, or the king, as the Mexicans called him, was the gigantic leader of a remarkable pack of grey wolves, that had ravaged the Currumpaw Valley for a number of years. All the shepherds and ranchmen knew him well, and, wherever he appeared with his trusty band, terror reigned supreme among the cattle, and wrath and despair among their owners. Old Lobo was a giant among wolves, and was cunning and strong in proportion to his size. His voice at night was well known and easily distinguished from that of any of his fellows. An ordinary wolf might howl half the night about the herdsman's bivouac without attracting more than a passing notice, but when the deep roar of the old king came booming down the canyon, the watcher bestirred himself and prepared to learn in the morning that fresh and serious inroads had been made among the herds.

Old Lobo's band was but a small one. This I never quite understood, for usually, when a wolf rises to the position and power that he had, he attracts a numerous following. It may be that he had as many as he desired, or perhaps his ferocious temper prevented the increase of his pack. Certain is it that Lobo had only five followers during the latter part of his reign. Each of these, however, was a wolf of renown, most of them were above the ordinary size—one in particular, the second in command, was a veritable giant, but even he was far below the leader in size and prowess. Several of the band, besides the two leaders, were especially noted. One of those was a beautiful white wolf, that the Mexicans called Blanca; this was supposed to be a female, possibly Lobo's mate. Another was a yellow wolf of remarkable swiftness, which, according to current stories, had on several occasions captured an antelope for the pack.

It will be seen, then, that these wolves were thoroughly well known to the cowboys and shepherds. They were frequently seen and oftener heard, and their lives were intimately associated with those of the cattlemen, who would so gladly have destroyed them. There was not a stockman on the Currumpaw who would not readily have given the value of many steers for the scalp of any one of Lobo's band, but they seemed to possess charmed lives and defied all manner of devices to kill them. They scorned all hunters, derided all poisons, and continued, for at least five years, to exact their tribute from the Currumpaw ranchers to the extent, many said, of a cow each day. According to this estimate, therefore, the band had killed more than two thousand of the finest stock, for, as was only too well known, they selected the best in every instance.

The old idea that a wolf was constantly in a starving state, and therefore ready to eat anything, was as far as possible from the truth in this case, for these freebooters were always sleek and well conditioned, and were in fact most fastidious about what they ate. Any animal that had died from natural causes, or that was diseased or tainted, they would not touch, and they even rejected anything that had been killed by the stockmen. Their choice and daily food was the tenderer part of a freshly killed yearling heifer. An old bull or cow they disdained, and though they occasionally took a young calf or colt, it was quite clear that veal or horseflesh was not their favourite diet. It was also known that they were not fond of mutton, although they often amused themselves by killing sheep. One night in November 1893 Blanca and the yellow wolf killed two hundred and fifty sheep, apparently for the fun of it, and did not eat an ounce of their flesh.

These are examples of many stories which I might repeat to show the ravages of this destructive band. Many new devices for their extinction were tried each year, but still they lived and throve in spite of all the efforts of their foes. A great price was set on Lobo's head, and in consequence poison in a score of subtle forms was put out for him, but he never failed to detect and avoid it. One thing only he feared—that was firearms, and knowing full well that all men in this region carried them, he never was known to attack or face a human being. Indeed, the set policy of his band was to take refuge in flight whenever, in the daytime, a man was descried, no matter at what distance. Lobo's habit of permitting the pack to eat only that which they themselves had killed was in numerous cases their salvation, and the keenness of his scent to detect the taint of human hands or the poison itself completed their immunity.

On one occasion, one of the cowboys heard the too familiar rallying cry of Old Lobo, and, stealthily approaching, he found the Currumpaw pack in a hollow, where they had 'rounded up' a small herd of cattle. Lobo sat apart on a knoll, while Blanca with the rest was endeavouring to 'cut out' a young cow which they had selected; but the cattle were standing in a compact mass with their heads outward, and presented to the foe a line of horns, unbroken save when some cow, frightened by a fresh onset of the wolves, tried to retreat into the middle of the herd. It was only by taking advantage of these breaks that the wolves had succeeded at all in wounding the selected cow, but she was far from being disabled, and it seemed that Lobo at

length lost patience with his followers, for he left his position on the hill and, uttering a deep roar, dashed toward the herd. The terrified rank broke at his charge, and he sprang in among them. Then the cattle scattered like the pieces of a bursting bomb. Away went the chosen victim, but ere she had gone twenty-five yards Lobo was upon her. Seizing her by the neck he suddenly held back with all his force and so threw her heavily to the ground. The shock must have been tremendous, for the heifer was thrown heels over head. Lobo also turned a somersault, but immediately recovered himself, and his followers, falling on the poor cow, killed her in a few seconds. Lobo took no part in the killing—after having thrown the victim he seemed to say, 'Now, why could not some of you have done that at once without wasting so much time?'

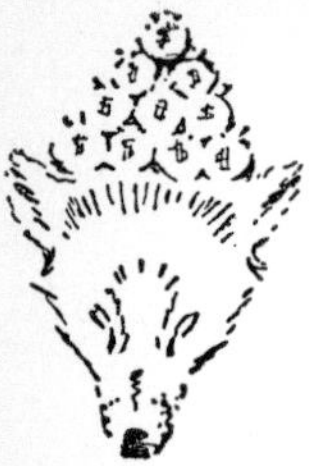

The man now rode up shouting, the wolves as usual retired, and he, having a bottle of strychnine, quickly poisoned the carcass in three places, then went away, knowing they would return to feed, as they had killed the animal themselves. But next morning, on going to look for his expected victims, he found that, although the wolves had eaten the heifer, they had carefully cut out and thrown aside all those parts that had been poisoned.

The dread of this great wolf spread yearly among the ranchmen, and each year a larger price was set on his head, until at last it reached $1,000, an unparalleled wolf-bounty, surely; many a good man has been hunted down for less. Tempted by the promised reward, a Texan ranger named Tannerey came one day galloping up the canyon of the Currumpaw. He had a superb outfit for wolf-hunting—the best of guns and horses, and a pack of enormous wolf-hounds. Far out on the plains of the Pan-handle he and his dogs had killed many a wolf, and now he never doubted that, within a few days, Old Lobo's scalp would dangle at his saddle-bow.

Away they went bravely on their hunt in the grey dawn of a summer morning, and soon the great dogs gave joyous tongue to say that they were already on the track of their quarry. Within two miles, the grizzly band of Currumpaw leaped into view, and the chase grew fast and furious. The part of the wolf-hounds was merely to hold the wolves at bay till the hunter could ride up and shoot them, and this usually was easy on the open plains of Texas; but here a new feature of the country came into play, and showed how well Lobo had chosen his range; for the rocky canyons of the Currumpaw and its tributaries intersect the prairies in every direction. The old wolf at once made for the nearest of these, and by crossing it got rid of the horsemen. His band then scattered and thereby scattered the dogs, and when they reunited at a distant point of course all of the dogs did not turn up, and the wolves, no longer outnumbered, turned on their pursuers and killed or desperately wounded them all. That night, when Tannerey mustered his dogs, only six of them returned, and of these two were terribly lacerated. This hunter made two other attempts to capture the royal scalp, but neither of them was more successful than the first, and in the last occasion his best horse met its death by a fall; so he gave up the chase in disgust and went back to Texas, leaving Lobo more than ever the despot of the region.

Next year two other hunters appeared, determined to win the promised bounty. Each believed he could destroy this noted wolf, the first by means of a newly devised poison, which was to be laid out in an entirely new manner; the other (a French Canadian), by poison assisted with certain spells and charms, for he firmly believed that Lobo was a veritable *loup-garou*, and could not be killed by ordinary means. But cunningly compounded poisons, charms and incantations were all of no avail against this grizzly devastator. He made his weekly rounds and daily banquets as aforetime and, before many weeks had passed, Calone and Laloche gave up in despair and went elsewhere to hunt.

In the spring of 1893, after his unsuccessful attempt to

capture Lobo, Joe Calone had a humiliating experience, which seems to show that the big wolf simply scorned his enemies, and had absolute confidence in himself. Calone's farm was on a small tributary of the Currumpaw, in a picturesque canyon, and among the rocks of this very canyon, within a thousand yards of the house, Old Lobo and his mate selected their den and raised their family that season. There they lived all summer, and killed Joe's cattle, sheep and dogs, but laughed at all his poisons and traps, and rested securely among the recesses of the cavernous cliffs, while Joe vainly racked his brain for some method of smoking them out, or of reaching them with dynamite. But they escaped entirely unscathed and continued their ravages as before. 'There's where he lived all last summer,' said Joe, pointing to the face of the cliff, 'and I couldn't do a thing with him. I was like a fool to him.'

II

THIS history, gathered so far from the cowboys, I found hard to believe until, in the fall of 1893, I made the acquaintance of the wily marauder, and at length came to know him more thoroughly than anyone else. Some years before, in the Bingo days, I had been a wolf-hunter, but my occupations since then had been of another sort, chaining me to stool and desk. I was much in need of a change, and when a friend, who was also a ranch owner on the Currumpaw, asked me to come to New Mexico and try if I could do anything with this predatory pack, I accepted the invitation and, eager to make the acquaintance of its king, was as soon as possible among the mesas of that region. I spent some time riding about to learn the country, and at intervals my guide would point to the skeleton of a cow, to which the hide still adhered, and remark, 'That's some of his work.'

It became quite clear to me that, in this rough country, it was useless to think of pursuing Lobo with hounds and horses, so that poison or traps were the only available expedients. At present we had no traps large enough, so I set to work with poison.

I need not enter into the details of a hundred devices that I employed to circumvent this *loup-garou*; there was no combination of strychnine, arsenic, cyanide or prussic acid that I did not essay; there was no manner of flesh that I did not try as bait; but morning after morning, as I rode forth to learn the result, I found that all my efforts had been useless. The old king was too cunning for me. A single instance will show his wonderful sagacity. Acting on the hint of an old trapper, I melted some cheese together with the kidney fat of a freshly killed heifer, stewing it in a china dish, and cutting it with a bone knife to avoid the taint of metal. When the mixture was cool I cut it into lumps, and, making a hole in one side of each lump, I inserted a large dose of strychnine and cyanide, contained in a capsule that was impermeable by any odour; finally I sealed the holes up with pieces of the cheese itself. During the whole process I wore a pair of gloves steeped in the hot blood of the heifer, and even avoided breathing on the baits. When all was ready I put them in a rawhide bag rubbed all over with blood, and rode forth dragging the liver and kidneys of the beef at the end of a rope. With this I made a ten-mile circuit, dropping a bait at each quarter of a mile, and taking the utmost care always not to touch any with my hands.

Lobo generally came into this part of the range in the early part of each week, and passed the latter part, it was supposed, around the base of Sierra Grande. This was Monday, and that same evening, as we were about to retire, I heard the deep bass howl of his majesty. On hearing it one of the boys briefly remarked, 'There he is—we'll see.'

The next morning I went forth, eager to know the result. I soon came on the fresh trail of the robbers, with Lobo in the lead—his track was always easily distinguished. An ordinary wolf's forefoot is $4\frac{1}{2}$ inches long, that of a large wolf $4\frac{3}{4}$ inches, but Lobo's, as measured a number of times, was $5\frac{1}{2}$ inches from claw to heel; I afterward found that his other proportions were commensurate, for he stood three feet high at the shoulder and weighed 150 pounds. His trail, therefore, though obscured by those of his followers, was never difficult to trace. The pack had soon found the track of my drag, and as usual followed it. I could see that Lobo had come to the first bait, sniffed about it and finally had picked it up.

Then I could not conceal my delight. 'I've got him at last!' I exclaimed. 'I shall find him stark within a mile!' And I galloped on with eager eyes fixed on the great broad track in the dust. It led me to the second bait, and that also was gone. How I exulted—I surely have him now, and perhaps several of his band! But there was the broad paw-mark still on the drag; and though I stood in the stirrup and scanned the plain I saw nothing that looked like a dead wolf. Again I followed—to find now that the third bait was gone—and the king-wolf's track led on to the fourth, there to learn that he had not really taken a bait at all, but had merely carried them in his mouth. Then, having piled the three on the fourth, he scattered filth over them to express his utter contempt for my devices. After this he left my drag and went about his business with the pack he guarded so effectively.

This is only one of many similar experiences which convinced me that poison would never avail to destroy this robber, and, though I continued to use it while awaiting the arrival of the traps, it was only because it was meanwhile a sure means of killing many prairie wolves and other destructive vermin.

About this time there came under my observation an incident that will illustrate Lobo's diabolic cunning. These wolves had at least one pursuit which was merely an amusement—it was stampeding and killing sheep, though they rarely ate them. The sheep are usually kept in flocks of from one thousand to three thousand, under one or more shep-

herds. At night they are gathered in the most sheltered place available, and a herdsman sleeps on each side of the flock to give additional protection. Sheep are such senseless creatures that they are liable to be stampeded by the veriest trifle, but they have deeply ingrained in their nature one, and perhaps only one, strong weakness, namely, to follow their leader. And this the shepherds turn to good account by putting half a dozen goats in the flock of sheep. The latter recognize the superior intelligence of their bearded cousins, and when a night alarm occurs they crowd around them and usually are thus saved from a stampede and are easily protected. But it was not always so. One night late in last November two Perico shepherds were aroused by an onset of wolves. Their flocks huddled around the goats which, being neither fools nor cowards, stood their ground and were bravely defiant; but, alas for them, no common wolf was heading this attack. Old Lobo, the werewolf, knew as well as the shepherds that the goats were the moral force of the flock, so, hastily running over the backs of the densely packed sheep, he fell on these leaders, slew them all in a few minutes and soon had the luckless sheep stampeding in a thousand different directions. For weeks afterward I was almost daily accosted by some anxious shepherd, who asked, 'Have you seen any stray OTO sheep lately?' and usually I was obliged to say I had; one day it was, 'Yes, I came on some five or six carcasses by Diamond Springs'; on another, it was to the effect that I had seen a small 'bunch' running on the Malpai Mesa; or again, 'No, but Juan Meira saw about twenty, freshly killed, on the Cedra Monte two days ago.'

At length the wolf-traps arrived, and with two men I worked a whole week to get them properly set out. We spared no labour or pains; I adopted every device I could think of that might help to ensure success. The second day after the traps arrived I rode around to inspect, and soon came upon Lobo's trail running from trap to trap. In the dust I could read the whole story of his doings that night. He had trotted along in the darkness and, although the traps were so carefully concealed, he had instantly detected the first one. Stopping the onward march of the pack, he had cautiously scratched around it until he had disclosed the trap, the chain and the log, then left them wholly exposed to view with the trap still unsprung; and passing on he treated over a dozen traps in the same fashion. Very soon I noticed that he stopped and turned aside as soon as he detected suspicious signs on the trail, and a new plan to outwit him at once suggested itself. I set the traps in the form of an H; that is, with a row of traps on each side of the trail, and one on the trail for the cross-bar of the H. Before long I had an opportunity to count another failure. Lobo came trotting along the trail, and was fairly between the parallel lines before he detected the single trap in the trail, but he stopped in time, and why or how he knew enough I cannot tell—the angel of the wild things must have been with him, but, without turning an inch to the right or left, he slowly and cautiously backed on his own tracks, putting each paw exactly in its old track until he was off the dangerous ground. Then returning at one side he scratched clods and stones with his hind feet till he had sprung every trap. This he did on many other occasions and, although I varied my methods and redoubled my precautions, he was never deceived, his sagacity seemed never at fault; and he might have been pursuing his career of rapine today but for an unfortunate alliance that proved his ruin and added his name to the long list of heroes who, unassailable when alone, have fallen through the indiscretion of a trusted ally.

III

Once or twice I had found indications that everything was not quite right in the Currumpaw pack. There were signs of irregularity, I thought; for instance there was clearly the trail of a smaller wolf running ahead of the leader at times,

and this I could not understand until a cowboy made a remark which explained the matter.

'I saw them today,' he said, 'and the wild one that breaks away is Blanca.'

Then the truth dawned upon me, and I added, 'Now, I know that Blanca is a she-wolf, because were a he-wolf to act thus Lobo would kill him at once.'

This suggested a new plan. I killed a heifer, and set one or two rather obvious traps about the carcass. Then cutting off the head, which is considered useless offal, and quite beneath the notice of a wolf, I set it a little apart and around it placed two powerful steel traps properly deodorized and concealed with the utmost care. During my operations I kept my hands, boots and implements smeared with fresh blood, and afterward sprinkled the ground with the same, as though it had flowed from the head; and when the traps were buried in the dust I brushed the place over with the skin of a coyote, and with a foot of the same animal made a number of tracks over the traps. The head was so placed that there was a narrow passage between it and some tussocks, and in this passage I buried two of my best traps, fastening them to the head itself.

Wolves have a habit of approaching every carcass they get the wind of, in order to examine it, even when they have no intention of eating of it. and I hoped that this habit would bring the Currumpaw pack within reach of my latest stratagem. I did not doubt that Lobo would detect my handiwork about the meat, and prevent the pack approaching it, but I did build some hopes on the head, for it looked as though it had been thrown aside as useless.

Next morning I sallied forth to inspect the traps, and there, oh, joy! were the tracks of the pack, and the place where the beef-head and its traps had been was empty. A hasty study of the trail showed that Lobo had kept the pack from approaching the meat, but one, a small wolf, had evidently gone on to examine the head as it lay apart and had walked right into one of the traps.

We set out on the trail, and within a mile discovered that the hapless wolf was Blanca. Away she went, however, at a gallop, and although encumbered by the beef-head, which weighed over fifty pounds, she speedily distanced my companion who was on foot. But we overtook her when she reached the rocks, for the horns of the cow's head became caught and held her fast. She was the handsomest wolf I had ever seen. Her coat was in perfect condition and nearly white.

She turned to fight and, raising her voice in the rallying cry of her race, sent a long howl rolling over the canyon. From far away upon the mesa came a deep response, the cry of Old Lobo. That was her last call, for now we had closed in on her, and all her energy and breath were devoted to combat.

Then followed the inevitable tragedy, the idea of which I shrank from afterward more than at the time. We each threw a lasso over the neck of the doomed wolf, and strained our horses in opposite directions until the blood burst from her mouth, her eyes glazed, her limbs stiffened and then fell limp. Homeward then we rode, carrying the dead wolf, and exulting over this, the first death blow we had been able to inflict on the Currumpaw pack.

At intervals during the tragedy, and afterward as we rode homeward, we heard the roar of Lobo as he wandered about on the distant mesas, where he seemed to be searching for Blanca. He had never really deserted her, but, knowing that he could not save her, his deep-rooted dread of firearms had been too much for him when he saw us approaching. All that day we heard him wailing as he roamed in his quest, and I remarked at length to one of the boys, 'Now indeed I truly know that Blanca was his mate.'

As evening fell he seemed to be coming toward the home canyon, for his voice sounded continually nearer. There was an unmistakable note of sorrow in it now. It was no longer the loud defiant howl, but a long plaintive wail. 'Blanca! Blanca!' he seemed to call. And as night came down I noticed that he was not far from the place where we had overtaken her. At length he seemed to find the trail and, when he came to the spot where we had killed her, his heart-broken wailing was piteous to hear. It was sadder than I could possibly have believed. Even the stolid cowboys noticed it, and said they had never heard a wolf carry on like that before. He seemed to know exactly what had taken place, for her blood had stained the place of her death.

Then he took up the trail of the horses and followed it to the ranch-house. Whether in hopes of finding her there, or in quest of revenge, I know not, but the latter was what he found, for he surprised our unfortunate watch-dog outside and tore him to little bits within fifty yards of the door. He evidently came alone this time, for I found but one trail next morning, and he had galloped about in a reckless manner that was very unusual with him. I had half expected this, and had set a number of additional traps about the pasture. Afterward I found that he had indeed fallen into one of these, but, such was his strength, he had torn himself loose and cast it aside.

I believed that he would continue in the neighbourhood until he found her body at least, so I concentrated all my energies on this one enterprise of catching him before he left the region, and while yet in this reckless mood. Then I realized what a mistake I had made in killing Blanca, for by using her as a decoy I might have secured him the next night.

I gathered in all the traps I could command, one hundred and thirty strong steel wolf-traps, and set them in fours in every trail that led into the canyon; each trap was separately fastened to a log, and each log was separately buried. In burying them I carefully removed the sod, and every particle of earth that was lifted we put in blankets, so that after the sod was replaced and all was finished the eye could detect no trace of human handiwork. When the traps were concealed I trailed the body of poor Blanca over each place, and made of it a drag that circled all about the ranch, and finally I took off one of her paws and made with it a line of tracks over each trap. Every precaution and device known to me I used, and retired at a late hour to await the result.

Once during the night I thought I heard Old Lobo, but was not sure of it. Next day I rode around, but darkness came on before I completed the circuit of the north canyon, and I had nothing to report. At supper one of the cowboys said, 'There was a great row among the cattle in the north canyon this morning; maybe there is something in the traps there.' It was afternoon of the next day before I got to the place referred to, and as I drew near a great grizzly form arose from the ground, vainly endeavouring to escape, and there revealed before me stood Lobo, King of the Currumpaw, firmly held in the traps. Poor old hero, he had never ceased to search for his darling, and when he found the trail her body had made he followed it recklessly, and so fell into the snare prepared for him. There he lay in the iron grasp of all four traps, perfectly helpless, and all around him were numerous tracks showing how the cattle had gathered about him to insult the fallen despot, without daring to approach within his reach. For two days and two nights he had lain there, and now was worn out with struggling. Yet, when I went near him, he rose up with bristling mane and raised his voice, and for the last time made the canyon reverberate with his deep bass roar, a call for help, the muster call of his band. But there was none to answer him, and, left alone in his extremity, he whirled about with all his strength and made a desperate effort to get at me. All in vain; each trap was a dead drag of over three hundred pounds, and in their relentless fourfold grasp, with great steel jaws on every foot, and the heavy logs and chains all entangled together, he was absolutely powerless. How his huge ivory tusks did grind on those cruel chains, and when I ventured to touch him with my rifle barrel he left grooves on it which are there to this day. His eyes glared green with hate and fury, and his jaws snapped with a hollow 'chop', as he vainly endeavoured to reach me and my trembling horse. But he was worn out with hunger and struggling and loss of blood, and he soon sank exhausted to the ground.

Something like compunction came over me, as I prepared to deal out to him that which so many had suffered at his hands.

'Grand old outlaw, hero of a thousand lawless raids, in a few minutes you will be but a great load of carrion. It cannot be otherwise.' Then I swung my lasso and sent it whistling over his head. But not so fast; he was yet far from being subdued, and before the supple coils had fallen on his neck he seized the noose and, with one fierce chop, cut through its hard thick strands, and dropped it in two pieces at his feet.

Of course I had my rifle as a last resource, but I did not wish to spoil his royal hide, so I galloped back to the camp and returned with a cowboy and a fresh lasso. We threw to our victim a stick of wood which he seized in his teeth, and before he could relinquish it our lassos whistled through the air and tightened on his neck.

Yet before the light had died from his fierce eyes I cried, 'Stay, we will not kill him; let us take him alive to the camp.' He was so completely powerless now that it was easy to put a stout stick through his mouth, behind his tusks, and then lash his jaws with a heavy cord which was also fastened to the stick. The stick kept the cord in, and the cord kept the stick in, so he was harmless. As soon as he felt his jaws were tied he made no further resistance, and uttered no sound, but looked calmly at us and seemed to say, 'Well, you have got me at last; do as you please with me.' And from that time he took no more notice of us.

We tied his feet securely, but he never groaned, nor

growled, nor turned his head. Then with our united strength we were just able to put him on my horse. His breath came evenly as though sleeping, and his eyes were bright and clear again, but did not rest on us. Afar on the great rolling mesas they were fixed, his passing kingdom, where his famous band was now scattered. And he gazed till the pony descended the pathway into the canyon, and the rocks cut off the view.

By travelling slowly we reached the ranch in safety, and after securing him with a collar and a strong chain we staked him out in the pasture and removed the cords. Then for the first time I could examine him closely, and proved how unreliable is vulgar report when a living hero or tyrant is concerned. He had *not* a collar of gold about his neck, nor was there on his shoulders an inverted cross to denote that he had leagued himself with Satan. But I did find on one haunch a great broad scar, that tradition says was the fang mark of Juno, the leader of Tannerey's wolf-hounds—a mark which she gave him the moment before he stretched her lifeless on the sand of the canyon.

I set meat and water beside him, but he paid no heed. He lay calmly on his breast, and gazed with those steadfast yellow eyes away past me down through the gateway of the canyon, over the open plains—his plains—nor moved a muscle when I touched him. When the sun went down he was still gazing fixedly across the prairie. I expected he would call up his band when night came, and prepared for them, but he had called once in his extremity, and none had come; he would never call again.

A lion shorn of his strength, an eagle robbed of his freedom, or a dove bereft of his mate—all die, it is said, of a broken heart; and who will aver that this grim bandit could bear the threefold brunt, heart-whole? This only I know, that when the morning dawned he was lying there still in his position of calm repose, his body unwounded, but his spirit was gone—the old king-wolf was dead.

I took the chain from his neck, a cowboy helped me to

carry him to the shed where lay the remains of Blanca; and as we laid him beside her the cattle-man exclaimed: 'There, you *would* come to her; now you are together again.'

Raggylug

The Story of a Cottontail Rabbit

RAGGYLUG, or Rag, was the name of a young cottontail rabbit. It was given him from his torn and ragged ear, a life-mark that he got in his first adventure. He lived with his mother in Olifant's Swamp, where I made their acquaintance and gathered, in a hundred different ways, the little bits of proof and scraps of truth that at length enabled me to write this history.

Those who do not know the animals well may think I have humanized them, but those who have lived so near them as to know somewhat of their ways and their minds will not think so.

Truly rabbits have no speech as we understand it, but they have a way of conveying ideas by a system of sounds, signs, scents, whiskertouches, movements and example that answers the purpose of speech; and it must be remembered that though in telling this story I freely translate from rabbit into English, *I repeat nothing that they did not say.*

I

THE rank swamp grass bent over and concealed the snug nest where Raggylug's mother had hidden him. She had partly covered him with some of the bedding, and, as always, her last warning was to 'lay low and say nothing, whatever happens'. Though tucked in bed, he was wide awake and his bright eyes were taking in that part of his little green world that was straight above. A blue-jay and a red squirrel, two notorious thieves, were loudly berating each other for stealing, and at one time Rag's home bush was the centre of their fight; a yellow warbler caught a blue butterfly but six inches from his nose, and a scarlet and black ladybug, serenely waving her knobbed feelers, took a long walk up one grass blade, down another, and across the nest and over Rag's face—and yet he never moved nor even winked.

After a while he heard a strange rustling of the leaves in the near thicket. It was an odd continuous sound, and though it went this way and that way and came ever nearer, there was no patter of feet with it. Rag had lived his whole life in the swamp (he was three weeks old) and yet had never heard anything like this. Of course his curiosity was greatly aroused. His mother had cautioned him to lay low, but that was understood to be in case of danger, and this strange sound without footfalls could not be anything to fear.

The low rasping went past close at hand, then to the right, then back, and seemed going away. Rag felt he knew what he was about; he wasn't a baby; it was his duty to learn what it was. He slowly raised his roly-poly body on his short fluffy legs, lifted his little round head above the covering of his nest and peeped out into the woods. The sound had ceased as soon as he moved. He saw nothing, so took one step forward to a clear view, and instantly found himself face to face with an enormous Black Serpent.

'Mammy!' he screamed in mortal terror as the monster darted at him. With all the strength of his tiny limbs he tried to run. But in a flash the snake had him by one ear and whipped around him with his coils to gloat over the helpless little baby bunny he had secured for dinner.

'Mam-my—Mam-my!' gasped poor little Raggylug as the cruel monster began slowly choking him to death. Very soon the little one's cry would have ceased, but bounding through the woods straight as an arrow came Mammy. No longer a shy helpless little Molly Cottontail, ready to fly from a shadow: the mother's love was strong in her. The cry of her baby had filled her with the courage of a hero, and—hop, she went over that horrible reptile. Whack, she struck down at him with her sharp hind claws as she passed, giving him such a stinging blow that he squirmed with pain and hissed with anger.

'M-a-m-m-y!' came feebly from the little one. And Mammy came leaping again and again and struck harder and fiercer until the loathsome reptile let go the little one's ear and tried to bite the old one as she leaped over. But all he got was a mouthful of wool each time, and Molly's fierce blows began to tell, as long bloody rips were torn in the Black Snake's scaly armour.

Things were now looking bad for the snake; bracing himself for the next charge, he lost his tight hold on Baby Bunny, who at once wriggled out of the coils and away into the underbrush, breathless and terribly frightened, but unhurt save that his left ear was much torn by the teeth of that dreadful serpent.

Molly now had gained all she wanted. She had no notion of fighting for glory or revenge. Away she went into the woods, and the little one followed the shining beacon of her snow-white tail until she led him to a safe corner of the swamp.

II

OLD Olifant's Swamp was a rough, brambly tract of second-growth woods, with a marshy pond and a stream through the middle. A few ragged remnants of the old forest still stood in it and a few of the still older trunks were lying about as dead logs in the brushwood. The land about the pond was of that willow-grown sedgy kind that cats and horses avoid, but that cattle do not fear. The drier zones were overgrown with briers and young trees. The outermost belt of all, that next the fields, was of thrifty, gummy-trunked young pines whose living needles in air and dead ones on earth offer so delicious an odour to the nostrils of the passer-by, and so deadly a breath to those seedlings that would compete with them for the worthless waste they grow on.

All around for a long way were smooth fields, and the only wild tracks that ever crossed these fields were those of a thoroughly bad and unscrupulous fox that lived only too near.

The chief indwellers of the swamp were Molly and Rag. Their nearest neighbours were far away and their nearest kin were dead. This was their home, and here they lived together, and here Rag received the training that made his success in life.

Molly was a good little mother and gave him a careful

bringing up. The first thing he learned was to 'lay low and say nothing'. His adventure with the snake taught him the wisdom of this. Rag never forgot that lesson; afterward he did as he was told, and it made the other things come more easily.

The second lesson he learned was 'Freeze'. It grows out of the first, and Rag was taught it as soon as he could run.

'Freezing' is simply doing nothing, turning into a statue. As soon as he finds a foe near, no matter what he is doing, a well-trained Cottontail keeps just as he is and stops all movement, for the creatures of the woods are of the same colour as the things in the woods and catch the eye only while moving. So when enemies chance together, the one who first sees the other can keep himself unseen by 'freezing' and thus have all the advantage of choosing the time for attack or escape. Only those who live in the woods know the importance of this; every wild creature and every hunter must learn it; all learn to do it well, but not one of them can beat Molly Cottontail in the doing. Rag's mother taught him this trick by example. When the white cotton cushion that she always carried to sit on went bobbing away through the woods, of course Rag ran his hardest to keep up. But when Molly stopped and 'froze', the natural wish to copy made him do the same.

But the best lesson of all that Rag learned from his mother was the secret of the brier bush. It is a very old secret now, and to make it plain you must first hear why the brier bush quarrelled with the beasts.

Long ago the roses used to grow on bushes that had no thorns. But the squirrels and mice used to climb after them, the cattle used to knock them off with their horns, the possum would twitch them off with his long tail, and the deer, with his sharp hoofs, would break them down. So the brier bush armed itself with spikes to protect its roses and declared eternal war on all creatures that climbed trees, or had horns, or hoofs, or long tails. This left the brier bush at peace with none but Molly Cottontail, who could not climb, was hornless, hoofless and had scarcely any tail at all.

In truth the Cottontail had never harmed a brier rose, and having now so many enemies the rose took the rabbit into especial friendship, and when dangers are threatening poor Bunny he flies to the nearest brier bush, certain that it is ready with a million keen and poisoned daggers to defend him.

So the secret that Rag learned from his mother was: 'The brier bush is your best friend.'

Much of the time that season was spent in learning the lay of the land, and the bramble and brier mazes. And Rag learned them so well that he could go all around the swamp by two different ways and never leave the friendly briers at any place for more than five hops.

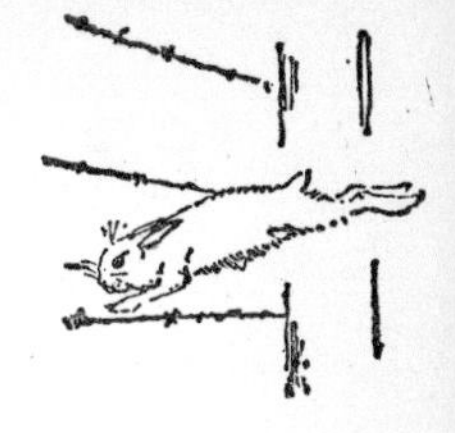

It is not long since the foes of the Cottontails were disgusted to find that man had brought a new kind of bramble and planted it in long lines throughout the country. It was so strong that no creatures could break it down, and so sharp that the toughest skin was torn by it. Each year there was more of it and each year it became a more serious matter to the wild creatures. But Molly Cottontail had no fear of it. She was not brought up in the briers for nothing. Dogs and foxes, cattle and sheep, and even man himself, might be torn by those fearful spikes: but Molly understands it and lives and thrives under it. And the farther it spreads the more safe country there is for the Cottontail. And the name of this new and dreaded bramble is—*the barbed-wire fence.*

III

Molly had no other children to look after now, so Rag had all her care. He was unusually quick and bright as well as strong, and he had uncommonly good chances; so he got on remarkably well.

All the season she kept him busy learning the tricks of the trail, and what to eat and drink and what not to touch. Day by day she worked to train him; little by little she taught him, putting into his mind hundreds of ideas that her own

life or early training had stored in hers, and so equipped with the knowledge that makes life possible to their kind.

Close by her side in the clover field or the thicket he would sit and copy her when she wobbled her nose 'to keep her smeller clear', and pull the bite from her mouth or taste her lips to make sure he was getting the same kind of fodder. Still copying her, he learned to comb his ears with his claws and to dress his coat and to bite burrs out of his vest and socks. He learned, too, that nothing but clear dewdrops from the briers were fit for a rabbit to drink, as water which has once touched the earth must surely bear some taint. Thus he began the study of woodcraft, the oldest of all sciences.

As soon as Rag was big enough to go out alone his mother taught him the signal code. Rabbits telegraph each other by thumping on the ground with their hind feet. Along the ground sound carries far; a thump that at six feet from the earth is not heard at twenty yards will, near the ground, be heard at least one hundred yards. Rabbits have very keen hearing, and so might hear this same thump at two hundred yards, and that would reach from end to end of Olifant's Swamp. A single *thump* means 'Look out' or 'Freeze'. A slow *thump thump* means 'Come'. A fast *thump thump* means 'danger'; and a very fast *thump thump thump* means 'Run for dear life'.

At another time, when the weather was fine and the bluejays were quarrelling among themselves, a sure sign that no dangerous foe was about, Rag began a new study. Molly, by flattening her ears, gave the sign to squat. Then she ran far away in the thicket and gave the thumping signal for 'Come'. Rag set out at a run to the place, but could not find Molly. He thumped, but got no reply. Setting carefully about his search, he found her foot scent and, following this strange guide, that the beasts all know so well and man does not know at all, he worked out the trail and found her where she was hidden. Thus he got his first lesson in trailing, and thus it was that the games of hide and seek they played became the schooling for the serious chase of which there was so much in his after life.

Before that first season of schooling was over he had learnt all the principal tricks by which a rabbit lives and in not a few problems showed himself a veritable genius.

He was an adept at 'tree', 'dodge', and 'squat', he could play 'log-lump', with 'wind' and 'balk' with 'back-track' so well that he scarcely needed any other tricks. He had not yet tried it, but he knew just how to play 'barbed wire', which is a new trick of the brilliant order; he had made a special study of 'sand', which burns up all scent, and he was deeply versed in 'change-off', 'fence', and 'double' as well as 'hole-up', which is a trick requiring longer notice, and yet he never forgot that 'lay-low' is the beginning of all wisdom and 'brier bush' the only trick that is always safe.

He was taught the signs by which to know all his foes and then the way to baffle them. For hawks, owls, foxes, hounds, curs, minks, weasels, cats, skunks, coons and men each have a different plan of pursuit, and for each and all of these evils he was taught a remedy.

And for knowledge of the enemy's approach he learnt to depend first on himself and his mother, and then on the blue-jay. 'Never neglect the blue-jay's warning,' said Molly. 'He is a mischief-maker, a marplot, and a thief all the time, but nothing escapes him. He wouldn't mind harming us, but he cannot, thanks to the briers, and his enemies are ours, so it is well to heed him. If the woodpecker cries a warning you can trust him, he is honest; but he is a fool beside the blue-jay, and though the blue-jay often tells lies for mischief you are safe to believe him when he brings ill news.'

The barbed-wire trick takes a deal of nerve and the best of legs. It was long before Rag ventured to play it, but as he came to his full powers it became one of his favourites.

'It's fine play for those who can do it,' said Molly. 'First you lead off your dog on a straight-away and warm him up a bit by nearly letting him catch you. Then keeping just one hop ahead, you lead him at a long slant full tilt into breast-high barbed wire. I've seen many a dog and fox crippled, and one big hound killed outright this way. But I've also seen more than one rabbit lose his life in trying it.'

Rag early learnt what some rabbits never learn at all, that 'hole-up' is not such a fine ruse as it seems; it may be the certain safety of a wise rabbit, but soon or late is a sure death-trap to a fool. A young rabbit always thinks of it first, an old rabbit never tries it till all others fail. It means escape from a man or dog, a fox or a bird of prey, but it means sudden death if the foe is a ferret, mink, skunk or weasel.

There were but two ground holes in the swamp—one on the sunning bank, which was a dry sheltered knoll in the south end. It was open and sloping to the sun, and here on fine days the Cottontails took their sunbaths. They stretched out among the fragrant pine needles and wintergreen in odd cat-like positions, and turned slowly over as though roasting and wishing all sides well done. And they blinked and panted and squirmed as if in dreadful pain; yet this was one of the keenest enjoyments they knew.

Just over the brow of the knoll was a large pine stump. Its grotesque roots wriggled out above the yellow sandbank like dragons, and under their protecting claws a sulky old woodchuck had dug a den long ago. He became more sour and ill tempered as weeks went by, and one day waited to quarrel with Olifant's dog instead of going in so that Molly Cottontail was able to take possession of the den an hour later.

This, the pine-root hole, was afterward very coolly taken by a self-sufficient young skunk who with less valour might have enjoyed greater longevity, for he imagined that even man with a gun would fly from him. Instead of keeping Molly from the den for good, therefore, his reign, like that of a certain Hebrew king, was over in seven days.

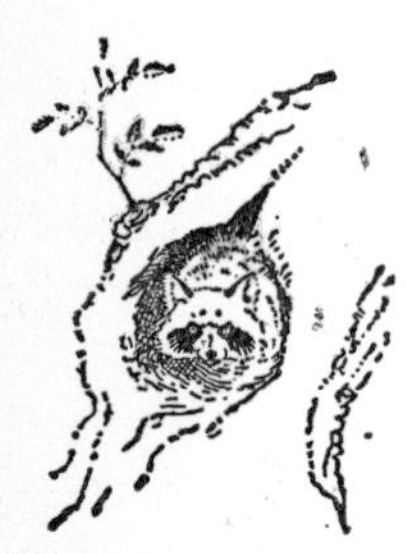

The other, the fern-hole, was in a fern thicket next the clover field. It was small and damp, and useless except as a last retreat. It also was the work of a woodchuck, a well-meaning friendly neighbour, but a harebrained youngster whose skin in the form of a whiplash was now developing higher horsepower in the Olifant working team.

'Simple justice,' said the old man, 'for that hide was raised on stolen feed that the team would a' turned into horsepower anyway.'

The Cottontails were now sole owners of the holes, and did not go near them when they could help it, lest anything like a path should be made that might betray these last retreats to an enemy.

There was also the hollow hickory which, though nearly fallen, was still green, and had the great advantage of being open at both ends. This had long been the residence of one Lotor, a solitary old coon whose ostensible calling was frog-hunting, and who, like the monks of old, was supposed to abstain from all flesh food. But it was shrewdly suspected that he needed but a chance to indulge in a diet of rabbit. When at last one dark night he was killed while raiding Olifant's hen-house, Molly, so far from feeling a pang of regret, took possession of his cosy nest with a sense of unbounded relief.

IV

BRIGHT August sunlight was flooding the swamp in the morning. Everything seemed soaking in the warm radiance. A little brown swamp sparrow was teetering on a long rush in the pond. Beneath him there were open spaces of dirty water that brought down a few scraps of the blue sky, and

worked it and the yellow duckweed into an exquisite mosaic, with a little wrong-side picture of the bird in the middle. On the bank behind was a great vigorous growth of golden green skunk cabbage, that cast dense shadow over the brown swamp tussocks.

The eyes of the swamp sparrow were not trained to take in the colour glories, but he saw what we might have missed: that two of the numberless leafy brown bumps under the broad cabbage leaves were furry living things, with noses that never ceased to move up and down whatever else was still.

It was Molly and Rag. They were stretched under the skunk cabbage, not because they liked its rank smell, but because the winged ticks could not stand it at all and so left them in peace.

Rabbits have no set time for lessons—they are always learning; but what the lesson is depends on the present stress, and that must arrive before it is known. They went to this place for a quiet rest, but had not been long there when suddenly a warning note from the ever-watchful blue-jay caused Molly's nose and ears to go up and her tail to tighten to her back. Away across the swamp was Olifant's big black and white dog, coming straight toward them.

'Now,' said Molly, 'squat while I go and keep that fool out of mischief.' Away she went to meet him and she fearlessly dashed across the dog's path.

'Bow-ow-ow!' he fairly yelled as he bounded after Molly, but she kept just beyond his reach and led him where the million daggers struck fast and deep, till his tender ears were scratched raw, and guided him at last plump into a hidden barbed-wire fence, where he got such a gashing that he went homewards howling with pain. After making a short double, a loop and a balk in case the dog should come back, Molly returned to find that Rag in his eagerness was standing bolt upright and craning his neck to see the sport.

This disobedience made her so angry that she struck him with her hind foot and knocked him over in the mud.

One day as they fed on the near clover field a red-tailed hawk came swooping after them. Molly kicked up her hind legs to make fun of him and skipped into the briers along one of their old pathways, where of course the hawk could not follow. It was the main path from the creekside thicket to the stove-pipe brush pile. Several creepers had grown across it, and Molly, keeping one eye on the hawk, set to work and cut the creepers off. Rag watched her, then ran on ahead, and cut some more that were across the path. 'That's right,' said Molly, 'always keep the runways clear: you will need them often enough. Not wide, but clear. Cut everything like a creeper across them and some day you will find you have cut a snare.'

'A what?' asked Rag, as he scratched his right ear with his left hind foot.

'A snare is something that looks like a creeper, but it doesn't grow and it's worse than all the hawks in the world,' said Molly, glancing at the now far-away red-tail, 'for there it hides night and day in the runway till the chance to catch you comes.'

'I don't believe it could catch me,' said Rag, with the pride of youth as he rose on his heels to rub his chin and whiskers high up on a smooth sapling. Rag did not know he was doing this, but his mother saw and knew it was a sign, like the changing of a boy's voice, that her little one was no longer a baby but would soon be a grown-up Cottontail.

V

There is magic in running water. Who does not know it and feel it? The railroad builder fearlessly throws his bank across the wide bog or lake, or the sea itself, but the tiniest rill of running water he treats with great respect, studies its wish and its way and gives it all it seems to ask. The thirst-parched traveller in the poisonous alkali deserts holds back in deadly fear from the sedgy ponds till he finds one down whose centre is a thin clear line, and a faint flow, the sign of running, living water; and joyfully he drinks.

There is magic in running water—no evil spell can cross it. Tam O'Shanter proved its potency in time of sorest need. The wild wood creature, with its deadly foe following tireless on the trail scent, realizes its nearing doom and feels an awful spell. Its strength is spent, its every trick is tried in vain till the good angel leads it to the water, the running, living water, and dashing in it follows the cooling stream, and then with force renewed takes to the woods again.

There is magic in running water. The hounds come to the very spot and halt and cast about; and halt and cast in vain. Their spell is broken by the merry stream, and the wild thing lives its life.

And this was one of the great secrets that Raggylug learned from his mother: 'After the brier rose the water is your friend.'

One hot muggy night in August, Molly led Rag through the woods. The cotton-white cushion she wore under her tail twinkled ahead and was his guiding lantern, though it went out as soon as she stopped and sat on it. After a few runs and stops to listen, they came to the edge of the pond. The hylas in the trees above them were singing '*Sleep, sleep*', and away out on a sunken log in the deep water, up to his chin in the cooling bath, a bloated bullfrog was singing the praises of a '*jug o' rum*'.

'Follow me still,' said Molly, in rabbit, and *flop* she went into the pond and struck out for the sunken log in the middle. Rag flinched, but plunged with a little 'Ouch!', gasping and wobbling his nose very fast but still copying his mother. The same movements as on land sent him through the water, and thus he found he could swim. On he went till he reached the sunken log and scrambled up by his dripping mother on the high dry end, with a rushy screen around them and the water that tells no tales. After this, in warm black nights when that old fox from Springfield came prowling through the swamp, Rag would note the place of the bullfrog's voice, for in case of direst need it might be a guide to safety. And thenceforth the words of the song that the bullfrog sang were, '*Come, come, in danger come.*'

This was the latest study that Rag took up with his mother—it was really a post-graduate course, for many little rabbits never learn it at all.

VI

No wild animal dies of old age. Its life has soon or late a tragic end. It is only a question of how long it can hold out against its foes. But Rag's life was proof that once a rabbit passes out of his youth he is likely to outlive his prime and be killed only in the last third of life, the downhill third we call old age.

The Cottontails had enemies on every side. Their daily life was a series of escapes. For dogs, foxes, cats, skunks, coons, weasels, minks, snakes, hawks, owls and men, and even insects, were all plotting to kill them. They had hundreds of adventures, and at least once a day they had to fly for their lives and save themselves by their legs and wits.

More than once that hateful fox from Springfield drove them to taking refuge under the wreck of a barbed-wire hog-pen by the spring. But once there they could look calmly at him while he spiked his legs in vain attempts to reach them.

Once or twice Rag when hunted had played off the hound against a skunk that had seemed likely to be quite as dangerous as the dog.

Once he was caught alive by a hunter who had a hound and a ferret to help him. But Rag had the luck to escape next day, with a yet deeper distrust of ground holes. He was several times run into the water by the cat, and many times was chased by hawks and owls, but for each kind of danger there was a safeguard. His mother taught him the principal dodges, and he improved on them and made many new ones as he grew older. And the older and wiser he grew the less he trusted to his legs and the more to his wits for safety.

Ranger was the name of a young hound in the neighbourhood. To train him his master used to put him on the trail of one of the Cottontails. It was nearly always Rag that they ran, for the young buck enjoyed the runs as much as they did, the spice of danger in them being just enough for zest. He would say:

'Oh, Mother, here comes the dog again! I must have a run today.'

'You are too bold, Raggy, my son!' she might reply. 'I fear you will run once too often.'

'But, Mother, it is such glorious fun to tease that fool dog, and it's all good training. I'll thump if I am too hard pressed, then you can come and change off while I get my second wind.'

On he would come, and Ranger would take the trail and follow till Rag got tired of it. Then he either sent a thumping telegram for help, which brought Molly to take charge of the dog, or he got rid of the dog by some clever trick. A description of one of these shows how well Rag had learned the arts of the woods.

He knew that his scent lay best near the ground, and was strongest when he was warm. So if he could get off the ground, and be left in peace for half an hour to cool off and for the trail to stale, he knew he would be safe. When therefore he tired of the chase, he made for the Creekside brier patch, where he 'wound'—that is, zigzagged—till he left a course so crooked that the dog was sure to be greatly delayed in working it out. He then went straight to D in the woods, passing one hop to windward of the high log E. Stopping at D, he followed his back trail to F, where he leaped and ran toward G. Then, returning on his trail to J, he waited till the hound passed on his trail at I. Rag then got back on his old trail at H, and followed it to E, where, with

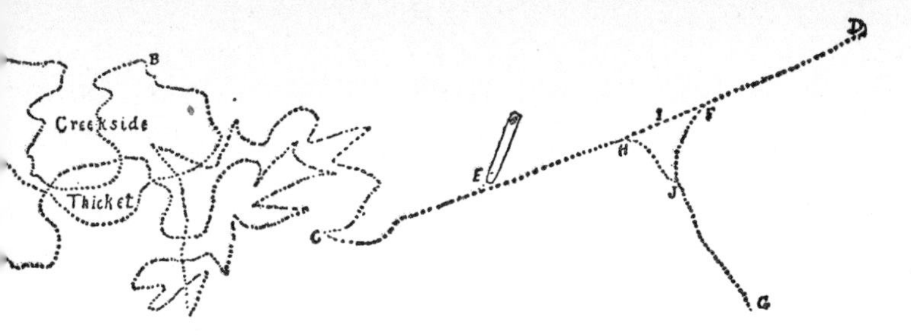

a scent-balk or great leap aside, he reached the high log, and, running to its higher end, he sat like a bump.

Ranger lost much time in the bramble maze, and the scent was very poor when he got it straightened out and came to D. Here he began to circle to pick it up, and after losing much time struck the trail which ended suddenly at G. Again he was at fault, and had to circle to find the trail. Wider and wider the circles, until at last he passed right under the log Rag was on. But a cold scent on a cold day does not go downward much. Rag never budged nor winked, and the hound passed.

Again the dog came round. This time he crossed the low part of the log, and stopped to smell it. Yes, clearly it was rabbity, but it was a stale scent now; still he mounted the log.

It was a trying moment for Rag, as the great hound came sniff-sniffing along the log. But his nerve did not forsake him; the wind was right; he had his mind made up to bolt as soon as Ranger came half way up. But he didn't come. A yellow cur would have seen the rabbit sitting there, but the hound did not, and the scent seemed stale, so he leaped off the log, and Rag had won.

VII

Rag had never seen any other rabbit than his mother. Indeed he had scarcely thought about there being any other. He was more and more away from her now, and yet he never felt lonely, for rabbits do not hanker for company. But one day in December, while he was among the red dogwood brush, cutting a new path to the great creekside thicket, he saw all at once against the sky over the sunning bank the head and ears of a strange rabbit. The newcomer had the air of a well-pleased discoverer and soon came hopping Rag's way along one of *his* paths into *his* swamp. A new feeling rushed over him, that boiling mixture of anger and hatred called jealousy.

The stranger stopped at one of Rag's rubbing trees—that is, a tree against which he used to stand on his heels and rub his chin as far up as he could reach. He thought he did this simply because he liked it; but all buck rabbits do so, and several ends are served. It makes the tree rabbity, so that other rabbits know that this swamp already belongs to a rabbit family and is not open for settlement. It also lets the next one know by the scent if the last caller was an acquaintance, and the height from the ground of the rubbing-places shows how tall the rabbit is.

Now to his disgust Rag noticed that the newcomer was a head taller than himself, and a big stout buck at that. This was a wholly new experience and filled Rag with a wholly new feeling. The spirit of murder entered his heart; he chewed very hard with nothing in his mouth, and hopping forward on to a smooth piece of hard ground he struck slowly, *Thump—thump—thump*, which is a rabbit telegram for 'Get out of my swamp or fight'.

The newcomer made a big V with his ears, sat upright for a few seconds, then, dropping on his fore-feet, sent along the ground a louder, stronger, *Thump—thump—thump*.

And so war was declared.

They came together by short runs sideways, each one trying to get the wind of the other and watching for a chance advantage. The stranger was a big heavy buck with plenty of muscle, but one or two trifles such as treading on a turnover and failing to close when Rag was on low ground showed that he had not much cunning and counted on winning his battles by his weight. On he came at last and Rag met him like a little fury. As they came together they leaped up and struck out with their hind feet. *Thud, thud* they came, and down went poor little Rag. In a moment the stranger was on him with his teeth and Rag was bitten, and lost several tufts of hair before he could get up. But he was swift of foot and got out of reach. Again he charged and again he was knocked down and bitten severely. He was no match for his foe, and it soon became a question of saving his own life.

Hurt as he was, he sprang away with the stranger in full chase and bound to kill him as well as to oust him from the swamp where he was born. Rag's legs were good and so was his wind. The stranger was big and so heavy that he soon gave up the chase, and it was well for poor Rag that he did, for he was getting stiff from his wounds as well as tired. From that day began a reign of terror for Rag. His training had been against owls, dogs, weasels, men and so on, but what to do when chased by another rabbit he did not know. All he knew was to lay low till he was found, then run.

Poor little Molly was completely terrorized; she could not help Rag, and sought only to hide. But the big buck soon found her out. She tried to run from him, but she was not now so swift as Rag. The stranger made no attempt to kill her, but he made love to her, and because she hated him and tried to get away he treated her shamefully. Day after day he worried her by following her about, and often, furious at her lasting hatred, he would knock her down and tear out mouthfuls of her soft fur till his rage cooled somewhat, when he would let her go for a while. But his fixed purpose was to kill Rag, whose escape seemed hopeless. There was no other swamp he could go to, and whenever he took a nap now he had to be ready at any moment to dash for his life. A dozen times a day the big stranger came creeping up to where he slept, but each time the watchful Rag awoke in time to escape. To escape yet not to escape. He saved his life indeed, but oh! what a miserable life it had become. How maddening to be thus helpless, to see his little mother daily beaten and torn, as well as to see all his favourite feeding-grounds, the cosy nooks and the pathways he had made with so much labour, forced from him by this hateful brute. Unhappy Rag realized that to the victor belong the spoils, and he hated him more than ever he did fox or ferret.

How was it to end? He was wearing out with running and watching and bad food, and little Molly's strength and spirit were breaking down under the long persecution. The stranger was ready to go to all lengths to destroy poor Rag, and at last stooped to the worst crime known among rabbits.

However much they may hate each other, all good rabbits forget their feuds when their common enemy appears. Yet one day, when a great goshawk came swooping over the swamp, the stranger, keeping well under cover himself, tried again and again to drive Rag into the open.

Once or twice the hawk nearly had him, but still the briers saved him, and it was only when the big buck himself came near being caught that he gave it up. And again Rag escaped, but was no better off. He made up his mind to leave with his mother, if possible, next night and go into the world in quest of some new home, when he heard old Thunder, the hound, sniffing and searching about the outskirts of the swamp, and he resolved on playing a desperate game. He deliberately crossed the hound's view, and the chase that then began was fast and furious. Thrice around the swamp they went, till Rag had made sure that his mother was hidden safely and that his hated foe was in his usual nest. Then right into that nest and plump over him he jumped, giving him a rap with one hind foot as he passed over his head.

'You miserable fool, I kill you yet!' cried the stranger,

and up he jumped only to find himself between Rag and the dog and heir to all the peril of the chase.

On came the hound baying hotly on the straight-away scent. The buck's weight and size were great advantages in a rabbit fight, but now they were fatal. He did not know many tricks—just the simple ones like 'double', 'wind', and 'hole-up', that every baby bunny knows. But the chase was too close for doubling and winding, and he didn't know where the holes were.

It was a straight race. The brier rose, kind to all rabbits alike, did its best, but it was no use. The baying of the hound was fast and steady. The crashing of the brush and the yelping of the hound each time the briers tore his tender ears were borne to the two rabbits where they crouched in hiding. But suddenly these sounds stopped, there was a scuffle, then loud and terrible screaming.

Rag knew what it meant and it sent a shiver through him, but he soon forgot that when all was over, and rejoiced to be once more the master of the dear old swamp.

VIII

OLD Olifant had doubtless a right to burn all those brush piles in the east and south of the swamp and to clear up the wreck of the old barbed-wire hog-pen just below the spring. But it was none the less hard on Rag and his mother. The first were their various residences and outposts, and the second their grand fastness and safe retreat.

They had so long held the swamp and felt it to be their very own in every part and suburb—including Olifant's grounds and buildings—that they would have resented the appearance of another rabbit even about the adjoining barnyard.

Their claim, that of long successful occupancy, was exactly the same as that by which most nations hold their land, and it would be hard to find a better right.

During the time of the January thaw the Olifants had cut the rest of the large wood about the pond and curtailed the Cottontails' domain on all sides. But they still clung to the dwindling swamp, for it was their home and they were loath to move to foreign parts. Their life of daily perils went on, but they were still fleet of foot, long of wind and bright of wit. Of late they had been somewhat troubled by a mink that had wandered upstream to their quiet nook. A little judicious guidance had transferred the uncomfortable visitor to Olifant's hen-house. But they were not yet quite sure that he had been properly looked after. So for the present they gave up using the ground holes, which were, of course, dangerous blind alleys, and stuck closer than ever to the briers and the brush piles that were left.

That first snow had quite gone and the weather was bright and warm until now. Molly, feeling a touch of rheumatism, was somewhere in the lower thicket seeking a tea-berry tonic. Rag was sitting in the weak sunlight on a bank in the east side. The smoke from the familiar gable chimney of Olifant's house came fitfully drifting a pale blue haze through the underwoods and showing as a dull brown against the brightness of the sky. The sun-gilt gable was cut off midway by the banks of brier brush, that purple in shadow shone like rods of blazing crimson and gold in the light. Beyond the house the barn with its gable and roof, new gilt as the house, stood up like a Noah's ark.

The sounds that came from it, and yet more the delicious smell that mingled with the smoke, told Rag that the animals were being fed cabbage in the yard. Rag's mouth watered at the idea of the feast. He blinked and blinked as he snuffed its odorous promises, for he loved cabbage dearly. But then he had been to the barnyard the night before after a few paltry clover tops, and no wise rabbit would go two nights running to the same place.

Therefore he did the wise thing. He moved across where he could not smell the cabbage and made his supper of a bundle of hay that had been blown from the stack. Later, when about to settle for the night, he was joined by Molly, who had taken her tea-berry and then eaten her frugal meal of sweet birch near the sunning bank.

Meanwhile the sun had gone about his business elsewhere, taking all his gold and glory with him. Off in the east a big black shutter came pushing up and rising higher and higher; it spread over the whole sky, shut out all light and left the world a very gloomy place indeed. Then another mischief-maker, the wind, taking advantage of the sun's absence, came on the scene and set about brewing trouble. The weather turned colder and colder; it seemed worse than when the ground had been covered with snow.

'Isn't this terribly cold? How I wish we had our stove-pipe brush pile,' said Rag.

'A good night for the pine-root hole,' replied Molly, 'but we have not yet seen the pelt of that mink on the end of the barn, and it is not safe till we do.'

The hollow hickory was gone—in fact at this very moment its trunk, lying in the wood-yard, was harbouring the mink they feared. So the Cottontails hopped to the south side of the pond and, choosing a brush pile, they crept under and snuggled down for the night, facing the wind but with their noses in different directions so as to go out different ways in case of alarm. The wind blew harder and colder as the hours went by, and about midnight a fine icy snow came ticking down on the dead leaves and hissing through the brush heap. It might seem a poor night for hunting, but that old fox from Springfield was out. He came pointing up the wind in the shelter of the swamp and chanced in the lee of the brush pile, where he scented the sleeping Cottontails. He halted for a moment, then came stealthily sneaking up toward the brush under which his nose told him the rabbits were crouching. The noise of the wind and the sleet enabled him to come quite close before Molly heard the faint crunch of a dry leaf under his paw. She touched Rag's whiskers, and both were fully awake just as the fox sprang on them; but they always slept with their legs ready for a jump. Molly darted out into the blinding storm. The fox missed his spring but followed like a racer, while Rag dashed off to one side.

There was only one road for Molly; that was straight up the wind, and bounding for her life she gained a little over the unfrozen mud that would not carry the fox, till she reached the margin of the pond. No chance to turn now—on she must go.

Splash! splash! through the weeds she went, then plunge into the deep water.

And plunge went the fox close behind. But it was too much for Reynard on such a night. He turned back, and Molly, seeing only one course, struggled through the reeds into the deep water and struck out for the other shore. But there was a strong head wind. The little waves, icy cold, broke over her head as she swam, and the water was full of snow that blocked her way like soft ice or floating mud. The dark line of the other shore seemed far, far away, with perhaps the fox waiting for her there.

But she laid her ears flat to be out of the gale, and bravely put forth all her strength with wind and tide against her. After a long weary swim in the cold water, she had nearly reached the farther reeds when a great mass of floating snow barred her road; then the wind on the bank made strange, fox-like sounds that robbed her of all force, and she was drifted far backward before she could get free from the floating bar.

Again she struck out, but slowly—oh, so slowly now. And when at last she reached the lee of the tall reeds, her limbs were numbed, her strength spent, her brave little heart was sinking and she cared no more whether the fox were there or not. Through the reeds she did indeed pass, but once in the weeds her course wavered and slowed, her feeble strokes no longer sent her landward, the ice forming around her stopped her altogether. In a little while the cold weak limbs ceased to move, the furry nosetip of the little mother

Cottontail wobbled no more and the soft brown eyes were closed in death.

But there was no fox waiting to tear her with ravenous jaws. Rag had escaped the first onset of the foe, and as soon as he regained his wits he came running back to change-off and so help his mother. He met the old fox going round the pond to meet Molly and led him far and away, then dismissed him with a barbed-wire gash on his head and came to the bank and sought about and trailed and thumped, but all his searching was in vain; he could not find his little mother. He never saw her again, and he never knew whither she went, for she slept her never-waking sleep in the ice-arms of her friend the Water that tells no tales.

Poor little Molly Cottontail! She was a true heroine, yet only one of unnumbered millions that without a thought of heroism have lived and done their best in their little world, and died. She fought a good fight in the battle of life. She was good stuff; the stuff that never dies. For flesh of her flesh and brain of her brain was Rag. She lives in him, and through him transmits a finer fibre to her race.

And Rag still lives in the swamp. Old Olifant died that winter, and the unthrifty sons ceased to clear the swamp or mend the wire fences. Within a single year it was a wilder place than ever; fresh trees and brambles grew, and falling wires made many Cottontail castles and last retreats that dogs and foxes dared not storm. And there to this day lives Rag. He is a big strong buck now and fears no rivals. He has a large family of his own and a pretty brown wife that he got I know not where. There, no doubt, he and his children's children will flourish for many years to come, and there you may see them any sunny evening, if you have learnt their signal code and, choosing a good spot on the ground, know just how and when to thump it.

Bingo

'Ye Franckelyn's dogge leaped over a style,
And yey yclept him lyttel Bingo,
B—I—N—G—O—,
And yey yclept him lyttel Bingo.

Ye Franckelyn's wyfe brewed nutte-brown
And he yclept ytte rare goode Stingo,
S—T—I—N—G—O—,
And he yclept ytte rare goode Stingo.

Now ys not this a prettye rhyme,
I thynke ytte ys bye Jingo,
J—I—N—G—O ,
I thynke ytte ys bye Jingo.'

Bingo

The Story of My Dog

I

It was early in November 1882, and the Manitoba winter had just set in. I was tilting back in my chair for a few lazy moments after breakfast, idly alternating my gaze from the one window-pane of our shanty, through which was framed a bit of the prairie and the end of our cowshed, to the old rhyme of the 'Franckelyn's dogge' pinned on the logs near by. But the dreamy mixture of rhyme and view was quickly dispelled by the sight of a large grey animal dashing across the prairie into the cowshed, with a smaller black and white animal in hot pursuit.

'A wolf!' I exclaimed, and seizing a rifle dashed out to help the dog. But before I could get there they had left the stable, and after a short run over the snow the wolf again turned at bay, and the dog, our neighbour's collie, circled about watching his chance to snap.

I fired a couple of long shots, which had the effect only of setting them off again over the prairie. After another run this matchless dog closed and seized the wolf by the haunch, but again retreated to avoid the fierce return chop. Then there was another stand at bay, and again a race over the snow. Every few hundred yards this scene was repeated, the dog managing so that each fresh rush should be toward the settlement, while the wolf vainly tried to break back toward the dark belt of trees in the east. At last after a mile of this fighting and running I overtook them, and the dog,

seeing that he now had good backing, closed in for the finish.

After a few seconds the whirl of struggling animals resolved itself into a wolf, on his back, with a bleeding collie gripping his throat, and it was now easy for me to step up and end the fight by putting a ball through the wolf's head.

Then, when this dog of marvellous wind saw that his foe was dead, he gave him no second glance, but set out at a lope for a farm four miles across the snow where he had left his master when first the wolf was started. He was a wonderful dog, and even if I had not come he undoubtedly would have killed the wolf alone, as I learned he had already done with others of the kind, in spite of the fact that the wolf, though of the smaller or prairie race, was much larger than himself.

I was filled with admiration for the dog's prowess and at once sought to buy him at any price. The scornful reply of his owner was, 'Why don't you try to buy one of the children?'

Since Frank was not in the market I was obliged to content myself with the next best thing, one of his alleged progeny. That is, a son of his wife. This probable offspring of an illustrious sire was a roly-poly ball of black fur that looked more like a long-tailed bear cub than a puppy. But he had some tan markings like those on Frank's coat that were, I hoped, guarantees of future greatness, and also a very characteristic ring of white that he always wore on his muzzle.

Having got possession of his person, the next thing was to find him a name. Surely this puzzle was already solved. The rhyme of the 'Franckelyn's dogge' was inbuilt with the foundation of our acquaintance, so with adequate pomp we 'yclept him lyttel Bingo'.

II

The rest of that winter Bingo spent in our shanty, living the life of a lubberly, fat, well-meaning, ill-doing puppy; gorging himself with food and growing bigger and clumsier each day. Even sad experience failed to teach him that he must keep his nose out of the rat-trap. His most friendly overtures to the cat were wholly misunderstood and resulted only in an armed neutrality that, varied by occasional reigns of terror, continued to the end; which came when Bingo, who early showed a mind of his own, got a notion for sleeping at the barn and avoiding the shanty altogether.

When the spring came I set about his serious education. After much pains on my behalf and many pains on his, he learned to go at the word in quest of our old yellow cow that pastured at will on the unfenced prairie.

Once he had learned his business he became very fond of it and nothing pleased him more than an order to go and fetch the cow. Away he would dash, barking with pleasure and leaping high in the air that he might better scan the plain for his victim. In a short time he would return driving her at full gallop before him, and gave her no peace until, puffing and blowing, she was safely driven into the farthest corner of her stable.

Less energy on his part would have been more satisfactory, but we bore with him until he grew so fond of this semi-daily hunt that he began to bring 'old Dunne' without being told. And at length not once or twice but a dozen times a day this energetic cowherd would sally forth on his own responsibility and drive the cow home to the stable.

At last things came to such a pass that whenever he felt like taking a little exercise, or had a few minutes of spare time, or even happened to think of it, Bingo would sally forth at racing speed over the plain and a few minutes later return, driving the unhappy yellow cow at full gallop before him.

At first this did not seem very bad, as it kept the cow

from straying too far; but soon it was seen that it hindered her feeding. She became thin and gave less milk; it seemed to weigh on her mind too, as she was always watching nervously for that hateful dog, and in the mornings would hang around the stable as though afraid to venture off and subject herself at once to an onset.

This was going too far. All attempts to make Bingo more moderate in his pleasure were failures, so he was compelled to give it up altogether. After this, though he dared not bring her home, he continued to show his interest by lying at her stable door while she was being milked.

As the summer came on the mosquitoes became a dreadful plague, and the consequent vicious switching of Dunne's tail at milking-time even more annoying than the mosquitoes.

Fred, the brother who did the milking, was of an inventive as well as an impatient turn of mind, and he devised a simple plan to stop the switching. He fastened a brick to the cow's tail, then set blithely about his work, assured of unusual comfort, while the rest of us looked on in doubt.

Suddenly through the mist of mosquitoes came a dull whack and an outburst of 'language'. The cow went on placidly chewing till Fred got on his feet and furiously attacked her with the milking-stool. It was bad enough to be whacked on the ear with a brick by a stupid old cow, but the uproarious enjoyment and ridicule of the bystanders made it unendurable.

Bingo, hearing the uproar, and divining that he was needed, rushed in and attacked Dunne on the other side. Before the affair quieted down the milk was spilt, the pail and stool were broken, and the cow and the dog severely beaten.

Poor Bingo could not understand it at all. He had long ago learned to despise that cow, and now in utter disgust he decided to forsake even her stable door, and from that time he attached himself exclusively to the horses and their stable.

The cattle were mine, the horses were my brother's, and

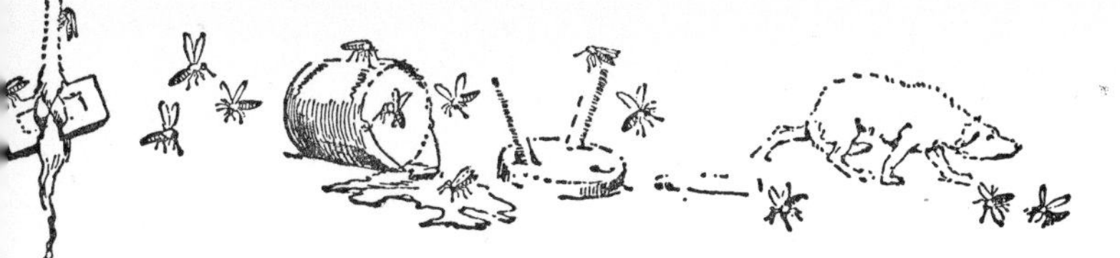

in transferring his allegiance from the cow-stable to the horse-stable Bingo seemed to give me up too, and anything like daily companionship ceased; and yet, whenever any emergency arose, Bingo turned to me and I to him, and both seemed to feel that the bond between man and dog is one that lasts as long as life.

The only other occasion on which Bingo acted as cow-herd was in the autumn of the same year at the annual Carberry Fair. Among the dazzling inducements to enter one's stock there was, in addition to a prospect of glory, a cash prize of two dollars for the best collie in training.

Misled by a false friend, I entered Bingo, and early on the day fixed the cow was driven to the prairie just outside of the village. When the time came she was pointed out to Bingo and the word given: 'Go fetch the cow.' It was the intention, of course, that he should bring her to me at the judge's stand.

But the animals knew better. They hadn't rehearsed all summer for nothing. When Dunne saw Bingo's careering form she knew that her only hope for safety was to get into her stable, and Bingo was equally sure that his sole mission in life was to quicken her pace in that direction. So off they raced over the prairie, like a wolf after a deer, and heading straight toward their home two miles away they disappeared from view.

That was the last that judge or jury ever saw of dog or cow. The prize was awarded to the only other entry.

III

Bingo's loyalty to the horses was quite remarkable; by day he trotted beside them, and by night he slept at the stable door. Where the team went Bingo went, and nothing kept him away from them. This interesting assumption of ownership lent the greater significance to the following circumstance.

I was not superstitious, and up to this time had had no faith in omens, but was now deeply impressed by a strange occurrence in which Bingo took a leading part. There were but two of us now living on the De Winton Farm. One morning my brother set out for Boggy Creek for a load of hay. It was a long day's journey there and back, and he made an early start. Strange to tell, Bingo for once in his life did not follow the team. My brother called to him, but still he stood at a safe distance and, eyeing the team askance, refused to stir. Suddenly he raised his nose in the air and gave vent to a long melancholy howl. He watched the wagon out of sight, and even followed for a hundred yards or so, raising his voice from time to time in the most doleful howlings. All that day he stayed about the barn, the only time that he was willingly separated from the horses, and at intervals howled a very death dirge. I was alone, and the dog's behaviour inspired me with an awful foreboding of calamity that weighed upon me more and more as the hours passed away.

About six o'clock Bingo's howlings became unbearable, so that for lack of a better thought I threw something at him, and ordered him away. But oh, the feeling of horror that filled me! Why did I let my brother go away alone? Should I ever again see him alive? I might have known from the dog's actions that something dreadful was about to happen.

At length the hour for his return arrived, and there was John on his load. I took charge of the horses, vastly relieved, and with an air of assumed unconcern asked, 'All right?'

'Right,' was the laconic answer.
Who now can say that there is nothing in omens?

And yet, when long afterwards I told this to one skilled in the occult, he looked grave and said, 'Bingo always turned to you in a crisis?'

'Yes.'

'Then do not smile. It was you that were in danger that day; he stayed and saved your life, though you never knew from what.'

IV

EARLY in the spring I had begun Bingo's education. Very shortly afterward he began mine.

Midway on the two-mile stretch of prairie that lay between our shanty and the village of Carberry was the corner-stake of the farm; it was a stout post in a low mound of earth, and was visible from afar.

I soon noticed that Bingo never passed without minutely examining this mysterious post. Next I learned that it was also visited by the prairie wolves as well as by all the dogs in the neighbourhood, and at length, with the aid of a telescope, I made a number of observations that helped me to an understanding of the matter and enabled me to enter more fully into Bingo's private life.

The post was by common agreement a registry of the canine tribes. Their exquisite sense of smell enabled each individual to tell at once by the track and trace what other had recently been at the post. When the snow came much more was revealed. I then discovered that this post was but one of a system that covered the country; that, in short, the entire region was laid out in signal stations at convenient intervals. These were marked by any conspicuous post, stone, buffalo skull, or other object that chanced to be in the desired locality, and extensive observation showed that it was a very complete system for getting and giving the news.

Each dog or wolf makes a point of calling at those stations that are near his line of travel to learn who has recently been there, just as a man calls at his club on returning to town and looks up the register.

I have seen Bingo approach the post, sniff, examine the ground about, then growl, and with bristling mane and glowing eyes scratch fiercely and contemptuously with his hind feet, finally walking off very stiffly, glancing back from time to time. All of which, being interpreted, said, '*Grrrh! woof!* There's that dirty cur of McCarthy's. *Woof!* I'll 'tend to him tonight. *Woof! woof!*'

On another occasion, after the preliminaries, he became keenly interested and studied a coyote's track that came and went, saying to himself, as I afterward learned:

'A coyote track coming from the north, smelling of dead cow. Indeed? Pollworth's old brindle must be dead at last. This is worth looking into.'

At other times he would wag his tail, trot about the vicinity and come again and again to make his own visit more evident, perhaps for the benefit of his brother Bill just back from Brandon! So that it was not by chance that one night Bill turned up at Bingo's home and was taken to the hills where a delicious dead horse afforded a chance suitably to celebrate the reunion.

At other times he would be suddenly aroused by the news, take up the trail, and race to the next station for later information.

Sometimes his inspection produced only an air of grave attention, as though he said to himself, 'Dear me, who the deuce is this?' or 'It seems to me I met that fellow at the Portage last summer.'

One morning on approaching the post Bingo's every hair stood on end, his tail dropped and quivered, and he gave proof that he was suddenly sick at the stomach—sure signs of terror. He showed no desire to follow up or know

more of the matter, but returned to the house, and half an hour afterward his mane was still bristling and his expression one of hate or fear.

I studied the dreaded track and learned that in Bingo's language the half-terrified, deep-gurgled '*grrr-wff*' means '*timber wolf*'.

These were among the things that Bingo taught me. And in the after time when I might chance to see him arouse from his frosty nest by the stable door and, after stretching himself and shaking the snow from his shaggy coat, disappear into the gloom at a steady trot trot, trot, I used to think:

'Aha! old dog, I know where you are off to, and why you eschew the shelter of the shanty. Now I know why your nightly trips over the country are so well timed, and how you know just where to go for what you want, and when and how to seek it.'

V

In the autumn of 1884 the shanty at De Winton Farm was closed and Bingo changed his home to the establishment—that is, to the stable, not the house—of Gordon Wright, our most intimate neighbour.

Since the winter of his puppyhood he had declined to enter a house at any time excepting during a thunderstorm. Of thunder and guns he had a deep dread—no doubt the fear of the first originated in the second, and that arose from some unpleasant shotgun experiences, the cause of which will be seen. His nightly couch was outside the stable, even during the coldest weather, and it was easy to see that he enjoyed to the full the complete nocturnal liberty entailed. Bingo's midnight wanderings extended across the plains for miles. There was plenty of proof of this. Some farmers at very remote points sent word to old Gordon that if he did not keep his dog home nights they would use the shotgun, and Bingo's terror of firearms would indicate that the threats were not idle. A man living as far away as Petrel said he saw a large black wolf kill a coyote on the snow one evening, but afterward he changed his opinion and 'reckoned it must 'a' been Wright's dog'. Whenever the body of a winter-killed ox or horse was exposed, Bingo was sure to repair to it nightly and, driving away the prairie wolves, feast to repletion.

Sometimes the object of a night foray was merely to maul some distant neighbour's dog and, notwithstanding vengeful threats, there seemed no reason to fear that the Bingo breed would die out. One man even avowed that he had seen a prairie wolf accompanied by three young ones which resembled the mother, excepting that they were very large and black and had a ring of white around the muzzle.

True or not as that may be, I know that late in March, while we were out in the sleigh with Bingo trotting behind, a prairie wolf was started from a hollow. Away it went with Bingo in full chase, but the wolf did not greatly exert itself to escape, and within a short distance Bingo was close up, yet strange to tell, there was no grappling, no fight!

Bingo trotted amiably alongside and licked the wolf's nose.

We were astounded, and shouted to urge Bingo on. Our shouting and approach several times started the wolf off at speed and Bingo again pursued until he had overtaken it, but his gentleness was too obvious.

'It is a she-wolf—he won't harm her!' I exclaimed as the truth dawned on me.

And Gordon said: 'Well, I be darned.'

So we called our unwilling dog and drove on.

For weeks after this we were annoyed by the depredations of a prairie wolf who killed our chickens, stole pieces of pork from the end of the house and several times terrified the children by looking into the window of the shanty while the men were away.

Against this animal Bingo seemed to be no safeguard.

At length the wolf, a female, was killed, and then Bingo plainly showed his hand by his lasting enmity toward Oliver, the man who did the deed.

VI

It is wonderful and beautiful how a man and his dog will stick to one another through thick and thin. Butler tells of an undivided Indian tribe in the Far North which was all but exterminated by an internecine feud over a dog that belonged to one man and was killed by his neighbour; and among outselves we have lawsuits, fights and deadly feuds, all pointing the same old moral, 'Love me, love my dog.'

One of our neighbours had a very fine hound that he thought the best and dearest dog in the world. I loved him, so I loved his dog and, when one day poor Tan crawled home terribly mangled and died by the door, I joined my threats of vengeance with those of his master, and thenceforth lost no opportunity of tracing the miscreant, both by offering rewards and by collecting scraps of evidence. At length it was clear that one of three men to the southward had had a hand in the cruel affair. The scent was warming up, and soon we should have been in a position to exact rigorous justice at least from the wretch who had murdered poor old Tan.

Then something took place which at once changed my mind and led me to believe that the mangling of the old hound was not by any means an unpardonable crime, but indeed on second thoughts was rather commendable than otherwise.

Gordon Wright's farm lay to the south of us, and while there one day, Gordon, jun., knowing that I was tracking the murderer, took me aside and, looking about furtively, he whispered in tragic tones:

'It was Bing done it.'

And the matter dropped right there. For I confess that

from that moment I did all in my power to baffle the justice I had previously striven so hard to further.

I had given Bingo away long before, but the feeling of ownership did not die; and of this indissoluble fellowship of dog and man he was soon to take part in another important illustration.

Old Gordon and Oliver were close neighbours and friends; they joined in a contract to cut wood, and worked together harmoniously till late on in winter. Then Oliver's old horse died and he, determining to profit as far as possible, dragged it out on the plain and laid poison baits for wolves around it. Alas, for poor Bingo! He would lead a wolfish life, though again and again it brought him into wolfish misfortunes.

He was as fond of dead horse as any of his wild kindred. That very night, with Wright's own dog Curley, he visited the carcass. It seemed as though Bing had busied himself chiefly keeping off the wolves, but Curley feasted immoderately. The tracks in the snow told the story of the banquet; the interruption as the poison began to work, and of the dreadful spasms of pain during the erratic course back home where Curley, falling in convulsions at Gordon's feet, died in the greatest agony.

'Love me, love my dog'; no explanations or apology were acceptable; it was useless to urge that it was accidental: the long standing feud between Bingo and Oliver was now remembered as an important tide-light. The wood contract was thrown up, all friendly relations ceased, and to this day there is no county big enough to hold the rival factions which were called at once into existence and to arms by Curley's dying yell.

It was months before Bingo really recovered from the poison. We believed indeed that he never again would be the sturdy old-time Bingo. But when the spring came he began to gain strength and, bettering as the grass grew, he was within a few weeks once more in full health and vigour to be a pride to his friends and a nuisance to his neighbours.

VII

CHANGES took me far away from Manitoba, and on my return in 1886 Bingo was still a member of Wright's household. I thought he would have forgotten me after two years' absence, but not so. One day early in the winter, after having been lost for forty-eight hours, he crawled home to Wright's with a wolf-trap and a heavy log fast to one foot, and the foot frozen to stony hardness. No one had been able to approach to help him, he was so savage, when I, the stranger now, stooped down and laid hold of the trap with one hand and his leg with the other. Instantly he seized my wrist in his teeth.

Without stirring I said, 'Bing, don't you know me?'

He had not broken the skin and at once released his hold and offered no further resistance, although he whined a good deal during the removal of the trap. He still acknowledged me his master in spite of his change of residence and my long absence, and notwithstanding my surrender of ownership I still felt that he was my dog.

Bing was carried into the house much against his will and his frozen foot thawed out. During the rest of the winter he went lame and two of his toes eventually dropped off. But before the return of warm weather his health and strength were fully restored, and to a casual glance he bore no mark of his dreadful experience in the steel trap.

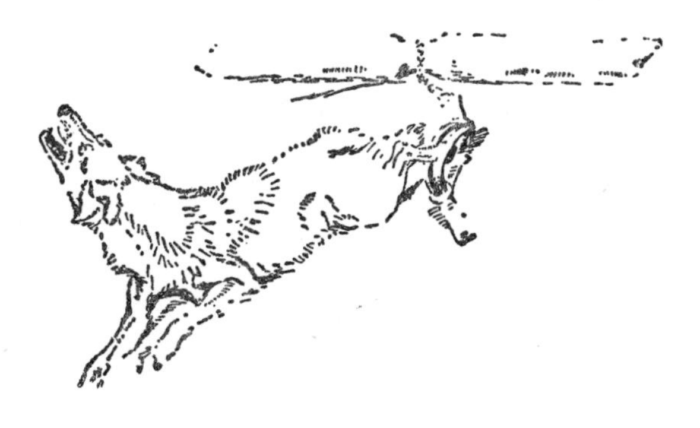

VIII

DURING that same winter I caught many wolves and foxes who did not have Bingo's good luck in escaping the traps, which I kept out right into the spring, for bounties are good even when fur is not.

Kennedy's Plain was always a good trapping ground because it was unfrequented by man and yet lay between the heavy woods and the settlement. I had been fortunate with the fur here, and late in April rode in on one of my regular rounds.

The wolf-traps are made of heavy steel and have two springs, each of one hundred pounds power. They are set in fours around a buried bait, and after being strongly fastened to concealed logs are carefully covered in cotton and in fine sand so as to be quite invisible.

A prairie wolf was caught in one of these. I killed him with a club and throwing him aside proceeded to reset the trap as I had done so many hundred times before. All was quickly done. I threw the trap-wrench over toward the pony and, seeing some fine sand near by, I reached out for a handful of it to add a good finish to the setting.

Oh, unlucky thought! Oh, mad heedlessness born of long immunity! That fine sand was *on the next wolf-trap*, and in an instant I was a prisoner. Although not wounded, for the traps have no teeth, and my thick trapping gloves deadened the snap, I was firmly caught across the hand above the knuckles. Not greatly alarmed at this, I tried to reach the trap-wrench with my right foot. Stretching out at full length, face downward I worked myself toward it, making my imprisoned arm as long and straight as possible. I could not see and reach at the same time, but counted on my toe telling me when I touched the little iron key to my fetters. My first effort was a failure; strain as I might at the chain my toe struck no metal. I swung slowly around my anchor, but still failed. Then a painfully taken observation showed I was much too far to the west. I set about working around,

tapping blindly with my toe to discover the key. Thus wildly groping with my right foot I forgot about the other till there was a sharp 'clank' and the iron jaws of trap No. 3 closed tight on my left foot.

The terrors of the situation did not, at first, impress me, but I soon found that all my struggles were in vain. I could not get free from either trap or move the traps together, and there I lay stretched out and firmly staked to the ground.

What would become of me now? There was not much danger of freezing for the cold weather was over, but Kennedy's Plain was never visited excepting by the winter woodcutters. No one knew where I had gone, and unless I could manage to free myself there was no prospect ahead but to be devoured by wolves, or else die of cold and starvation.

As I lay there the red sun went down over the spruce swamp west of the plain, and a shorelark on a gopher mound a few yards off twittered his evening song, just as one had done the night before at our shanty door, and though the numb pains were creeping up my arm, and a deadly chill possessed me, I noticed how long his little ear-tufts were. Then my thoughts went to the comfortable supper table at Wright's shanty, and I thought, now they are frying the pork for supper, or just sitting down. My pony still stood as I left him with his bridle on the ground patiently waiting to take me home. He did not understand the long delay, and when I called he ceased nibbling the grass and looked at me in dumb, helpless inquiry. If he would only go home the empty saddle might tell the tale and bring help. But his very faithfulness kept him waiting hour after hour while I was perishing of cold and hunger.

Then I remembered how old Girou the trapper had been lost, and in the following spring his comrades found his skeleton held by the leg in a bear-trap. I wondered which part of my clothing would show my identity. Then a new thought came to me. This is how a wolf feels when he is trapped. Oh, what misery have I been responsible for! Now I'm to pay for it.

Night came slowly on. A prairie wolf howled, the pony pricked up his ears and, walking nearer to me, stood with his head down. Then another prairie wolf howled and another, and I could make out that they were gathering in the neighbourhood. There I lay prone and helpless, wondering if it would not be strictly just that they should come and tear me to pieces. I heard them calling for a long time before I realized that dim shadowy forms were sneaking near. The horse saw them first, and his terrified snort drove them back at first, but they came near next time and sat around me on the prairie. Soon one bolder than the others crawled up and tugged at the body of his dead relative. I shouted and he retreated growling. The pony ran to a distance in terror. Presently the wolf returned, and after two or three of these retreats and returns the body was dragged off and devoured by the rest in a few minutes.

After this they gathered nearer and sat on their haunches to look at me, and the boldest one smelt the rifle and scratched dirt on it. He retreated when I kicked at him with my free foot and shouted, but growing bolder as I grew weaker he came and snarled right in my face. At this several others snarled and came up closer, and I realized that I was to be devoured by the foe that I most despised, when suddenly out of the gloom with a guttural roar sprang a great black wolf. The prairie wolves scattered like chaff, except the bold one, which, seized by the black newcomer, was in a few moments a draggled corpse; and then, oh horrors! this mighty brute bounded at me and—Bingo, noble Bingo, rubbed his shaggy panting sides against me and licked my cold face.

'Bingo—Bing—old—boy—fetch me the trap-wrench!'

Away he went and returned dragging the rifle, for he knew only that I wanted something.

'No—Bing—the trap-wrench.' This time it was my sash, but at last he brought the wrench, and wagged his tail in joy that it was right. Reaching out with my free hand, after much difficulty I unscrewed the pillar-nut. The trap fell apart and my hand was released, and a minute later I was free. Bing brought the pony up, and after slowly walking to restore the circulation I was able to mount. Then, slowly at first but soon at a gallop, with Bingo as herald careering and barking ahead, we set out for home, there to learn that the night before, though never taken on the trapping rounds, the brave dog had acted strangely, whimpering and watching the timber trail; and at last when night came on, in spite of attempts to detain him he had set out in the gloom and, guided by a knowledge that is beyond us, had reached the spot in time to avenge me as well as set me free.

Staunch old Bing—he was a strange dog. Though his heart was with me, he passed me next day with scarcely a look, but responded with alacrity when little Gordon called him to a gopher hunt. And it was so to the end; and to the end also he lived the wolfish life that he loved, and never failed to seek the winter-killed horses and found one again with a poisoned bait, and wolfishly bolted that; then feeling the pang, set out, not for Wright's but to find me, and reached the door of my shanty where I should have been. Next day on returning I found him dead in the snow with his head on the sill of the door—the door of his puppyhood's days; my dog to the last in his heart of hearts—it was my help he sought, and vainly sought, in the hour of his bitter extremity.

The Springfield Fox

I

THE hens had been mysteriously disappearing for over a month; and when I came home to Springfield for the summer holidays it was my duty to find the cause. This was soon done. The fowls were carried away bodily one at a time, before going to roost or else after leaving, which put tramps and neighbours out of court; they were not taken from the high perches, which cleared all coons and owls; or left partly eaten, so that weasels, skunks or minks were not the guilty ones, and the blame, therefore, was surely left at Reynard's door.

The great pine wood of Erindale was on the other bank of the river, and on looking carefully about the lower ford I saw a few fox tracks and a barred feather from one of our Plymouth Rock chickens. On climbing the farther bank in search of more clues, I heard a great outcry of crows behind me and, turning, saw a number of these birds darting down at something in the ford. A better view showed that it was the old story, thief catch thief, for there in the middle of the ford was a fox with something in his jaws—he was returning from our barnyard with another hen. The crows, though shameless robbers themselves, are ever first to cry 'Stop thief', and yet more than ready to take 'hush-money' in the form of a share in the plunder.

And this was their game now. The fox to get back home must cross the river, where he was exposed to the full brunt of the crow mob. He made a dash for it, and would doubtless

have got across with his booty had I not joined in the attack, whereupon he dropped the hen, scarce dead, and disappeared in the woods.

This large and regular levy of provisions wholly carried off could mean but one thing, a family of little foxes at home; and to find them I now was bound.

That evening I went with Ranger, my hound, across the river into the Erindale woods. As soon as the hound began to circle we heard the short sharp bark of a fox from a thickly wooded ravine close by. Ranger dashed in at once, struck a hot scent and went off on a lively straight-away till his voice was lost in the distance away over the upland.

After nearly an hour he came back, panting and warm, for it was baking August weather, and lay down at my feet.

But almost immediately the same foxy '*Yap yurrr*' was heard close at hand, and off dashed the dog on another chase.

Away he went in the darkness, baying like a foghorn, straight away to the north. And the loud '*Boo, boo*' became a low '*oo, oo*', and that a feeble '*o-o*' and then was lost. They must have gone some miles away, for even with ear to the ground I heard nothing of them, though a mile was easy distance for Ranger's brazen voice.

As I waited in the black woods I heard a sweet sound of dripping water: *Tink tank tenk tink, Ta tink tank tenk tonk.*

I did not know of any spring so near, and in the hot night it was a glad find. But the sound led me to the bough of an oak tree, where I found its source. Such a soft sweet song; full of delightful suggestion on such a night:

Tonk tank tenk tink
Ta tink a tonk a tank a tink a
Ta ta tink tank ta ta tonk tink
Drink a tank a drink a drunk.

It was the 'water-dripping' song of the saw-whet owl.

But suddenly a deep raucous breathing and a rustle of leaves showed that Ranger was back. He was completely fagged out. His tongue hung almost to the ground and was dripping with foam, his flanks were heaving and spume flecks dribbled from his breast and sides. He stopped panting a moment to give my hand a dutiful lick, then flung himself flop on the leaves to drown all other sounds with his noisy panting.

But again that tantalizing '*Yap yurrr*' was heard a few feet away, and the meaning of it all dawned on me.

We were close to the den where the little foxes were, and the old ones were taking turns in trying to lead us away.

It was late night now, so we went home feeling sure that the problem was nearly solved.

II

It was well known that there was an old fox with his family living in the neighbourhood, but no one supposed them so near.

This fox had been called 'Scarface', because of a scar reaching from his eye through and behind his ear; this was supposed to have been given him by a barbed-wire fence during a rabbit hunt and, as the hair came in white after it healed, it was always a strong mark.

The winter before I had met with him and had had a sample of his craftiness. I was out shooting, after a fall of snow, and had crossed the open fields to the edge of the brushy hollow at the back of the old mill. As my head rose to a view of the hollow I caught sight of a fox trotting at long range down the other side, in line to cross my course. Instantly I held motionless, and did not even lower or turn my head lest I should catch his eye by moving, until he went on out of sight in the thick cover at the bottom. As soon as he was hidden I bobbed down and ran to head him off where he should leave the cover on the other side, and was there in good time waiting, but no fox came forth. A careful look showed the fresh track of a fox that had bounded from the cover, and following it with my eye I saw old Scarface himself far out of range behind me, sitting on his haunches and grinning as though much amused.

A study of the trail made all clear. He had seen me at the moment I saw him, but he, also like a true hunter, had concealed the fact, putting on an air of unconcern till out of sight, when he had run for his life around behind me and amused himself by watching my stillborn trick.

In the spring time I had yet another instance of Scarface's cunning. I was walking with a friend along the road over the high pasture. We passed within thirty feet of a ridge on which were several grey and brown boulders. When at the nearest point my friend said:

'Stone number three looks to me very much like a fox curled up.'

But I could not see it, and we passed. We had not gone many yards farther when the wind blew on his boulder as on fur.

My friend said, 'I am sure that is a fox, lying asleep.'

'We'll soon settle that,' I replied, and turned back, but as soon as I had taken one step from the road up jumped Scarface—for it was he—and ran. A fire had swept the middle of the pasture, leaving a broad belt of black; over this he scurried till he came to the unburnt yellow grass again, where he squatted down and was lost in view. He had been watching us all the time, and would not have moved had we kept to the road. The wonderful part of this is, not that he resembled the round stones and dry grass, but that he *knew he did*, and was ready to profit by it.

We soon found that it was Scarface and his wife Vixen that had made our woods their home and our barnyard their base of supplies.

Next morning a search in the pines showed a great bank of earth that had been scratched up within a few months. It must have come from a hole, and yet there was none to be seen. It is well known that a really cute fox, on digging a new den, brings all the earth out at the first hole made, but carries on a tunnel into some distant thicket. Then closing up for good the first made and too well marked door, he uses only the entrance hidden in the thicket.

So after a little search at the other side of a knoll I found the real entry and good proof that there was a nest of little foxes inside.

Rising above the brush on the hillside was a great hollow basswood. It leaned a good deal and had a large hole at the bottom, and a smaller one at top.

We boys had often used this tree in playing Swiss Family Robinson, and by cutting steps in its soft punky walls had made it easy to go up and down in the hollow. Now it came in handy, for next day when the sun was warm I went there to watch, and from this perch on the roof I soon saw the interesting family that lived in the cellar near by. There were four little foxes; they looked curiously like little lambs, with their woolly coats, their long thick legs and innocent expressions, and yet a second glance at their broad, sharp-nosed, sharp-eyed visages showed that each of these innocents was the makings of a crafty old fox.

They played about, basking in the sun, or wrestling with each other till a slight sound made them scurry underground. But their alarm was needless, for the cause of it was their mother; she stepped from the bushes bringing another hen—number seventeen, as I remember. A low call from her and the little fellows came tumbling out. Then began a scene that I thought charming, but which my uncle would not have enjoyed at all.

They rushed on the hen, and tussled and fought with it, and each other, while the mother, keeping a sharp eye for enemies, looked on with fond delight. The expression on her face was remarkable. It was first a grinning of delight, but her usual look of wildness and cunning was there, nor were cruelty and nervousness lacking, but over all was the unmistakable look of the mother's pride and love.

The base of my tree was hidden in bushes and much lower than the knoll where the den was. So I could come and go at will without scaring the foxes.

For many days I went there and saw much of the training of the young ones. They early learned to turn to statuettes at any strange sound, and then on hearing it again or finding other cause for fear to run for shelter.

Some animals have so much mother love that it overflows and benefits outsiders. Not so old Vixen, it would seem. Her pleasure in the cubs led to most refined cruelty. For she often brought home to them mice and birds alive, and with diabolic gentleness would avoid doing them serious hurt so that the cubs might have larger scope to torment them.

There was a woodchuck that lived over in the hill orchard. He was neither handsome nor interesting, but he knew how to take care of himself. He had dug a den between the roots of an old pine stump, so that the foxes could not follow him by digging. But hard work was not their way of life; wits they believed worth more than elbow-grease. This woodchuck usually sunned himself on the stump each morning. If he saw a fox near he went down in the door of his den, or if the enemy was very near he went inside and stayed long enough for the danger to pass.

One morning Vixen and her mate seemed to decide that it was time the children knew something about the broad subject of woodchucks, and further that this orchard woodchuck would serve nicely for an object lesson. So they went together to the orchard fence unseen by old Chuckie on his stump. Scarface then showed himself in the orchard and quietly walked in a line so as to pass by the stump at a distance, but never once turned his head or allowed the ever watchful woodchuck to think himself seen. When the fox entered the field the woodchuck quietly dropped down to the mouth of his den; here he waited as the fox passed, but, concluding that after all wisdom is the better part, went into his hole.

This was what the foxes wanted. Vixen had kept out of sight, but now ran swiftly to the stump and hid behind it. Scarface had kept straight on, going very slowly. The

woodchuck had not been frightened, so before long his head popped up between the roots and he looked around. There was that fox still going on, farther and farther away. The woodchuck grew bold as the fox went, and came out farther and then, seeing the coast clear he scrambled on to the stump, and with one spring Vixen had him and shook him till he lay senseless. Scarface had watched out of the corner of his eye and now came running back. But Vixen took the chuck in her jaws and made for the den, so he saw he wasn't needed.

Back to the den came Vix, and carried the chuck so carefully that he was able to struggle a little when she got there. A low '*woof*' at the den brought the little fellows out like schoolboys to play. She threw the wounded animal to them and they set on him like four little furies, uttering little growls and biting little bites with all the strength of their baby jaws, but the woodchuck fought for his life and beating them off slowly hobbled to the shelter of a thicket. The little ones pursued like a pack of hounds and dragged at his tail and flanks, but could not hold him back. So Vix overtook him with a couple of bounds and dragged him again into the open for the children to worry. Again and again this rough sport went on till one of the little ones was badly bitten, and his squeal of pain roused Vix to end the woodchuck's misery and serve him up at once.

Not far from the den was a hollow overgrown with coarse grass, the playground of a colony of field-mice. The earliest lesson in woodcraft that the little ones took, away from the den, was in this hollow. Here they had their first course of mice, the easiest of all game. In teaching, the main thing was example, aided by a deep-set instinct. The old fox also had one or two signs meaning 'Lie still and watch', 'Come, do as I do' and so on, that were much used.

So the merry lot went to this hollow one calm evening and Mother Fox made them lie still in the grass. Presently a faint squeak showed that the game was astir. Vix rose up and went on tiptoe into the grass—not crouching, but as high as she could stand, sometimes on her hind legs so as to get a better view. The runs that the mice follow are hidden under the grass tangle, and the only way to know the whereabouts of a mouse is by seeing the slight shaking of the grass, which is the reason why mice are hunted only on calm days.

And the trick is to locate the mouse and seize him first and see him afterwards. Vix soon made a spring, and in the middle of the bunch of dead grass that she grabbed was a field-mouse squeaking his last squeak.

He was soon gobbled, and the four awkward little foxes tried to do the same as their mother, and when at length the eldest for the first time in his life caught game, he quivered with excitement and ground his pearly little milk-teeth into the mouse with a rush of inborn savageness that must have surprised even himself.

Another home lesson was on the red squirrel. One of these noisy vulgar creatures lived close by, and used to waste part of each day scolding the foxes from some safe perch. The cubs made many vain attempts to catch him as he ran across their glade from one tree to another, or spluttered and scolded at them a foot or so out of reach. But old Vixen was up in natural history—she knew squirrel nature and took the case in hand when the proper time came. She hid the children and lay down flat in the middle of the open glade. The saucy low-minded squirrel came and scolded as usual. But she moved no hair. He came nearer and at last right overhead to chatter:

'You brute you, you brute you.'

But Vix lay as dead. This was very perplexing, so the squirrel came down the trunk and peeping about made a nervous dash across the grass, to another tree, again to scold from a safe perch.

'You brute you, you useless brute, scarrr-scarrrr.'

But flat and lifeless on the grass lay Vix. This was most tantalizing to the squirrel. He was naturally curious and disposed to be venturesome, so again he came to the ground and scurried across the glade nearer than before.

Still as death lay Vix; surely she was dead. And the little foxes began to wonder if their mother wasn't asleep.

But the squirrel was working himself into a little craze of foolhardy curiosity. He had dropped a piece of bark on Vix's head, he had used up his list of bad words and he had done it all over again, without getting a sign of life. So after a couple more dashes across the glade he ventured within a few feet of the really watchful Vix, who sprang to her feet and pinned him in a twinkling.

'And the little ones picked his bones e-oh!'

Thus the rudiments of their education were laid, and afterward as they grew stronger they were taken farther afield to begin the higher branches of trailing and scenting.

For each kind of prey they were taught a way to hunt, for every animal has some great strength or it could not live, and some great weakness or the others could not live. The squirrel's weakness was foolish curiosity; the fox's that he can't climb a tree. And the training of the little foxes was all shaped to take advantage of the weakness of the other creatures and to make up for their own by defter play where they are strong.

From their parents they learned the chief axioms of the fox world. How, is not easy to say. But that they learned this in company with their parents was clear. Here are some that foxes taught me, without saying a word:

Never sleep on your straight track.
Your nose is before your eyes, then trust it first.
A fool runs down the wind.
Running rills cure many ills.
Never take the open if you can keep the cover.
Never leave a straight trail if a crooked one will do.
If it's strange, it's hostile.
Dust and water burn the scent.
Never hunt mice in a rabbit-woods, or rabbits in a hen-yard.

Keep off the grass.

Inklings of the meanings of these were already entering the little ones' minds—thus, 'Never follow what you can't smell,' was wise, they could see, because if you can't smell it, then the wind is so that it must smell you.

One by one they learned the birds and beasts of their home woods, and then as they were able to go abroad with their parents they learned new animals. They were beginning to think they knew the scent of everything that moved. But one night the mother took them to a field where was a strange black flat thing on the ground. She brought them on purpose to smell it, but at the first whiff their every hair stood on end, they trembled, they knew not why—it seemed to tingle through their blood and fill them with instinctive hate and fear. And when she saw its full effect she told them:

'*That is man scent.*'

III

MEANWHILE the hens continued to disappear. I had not betrayed the den of cubs. Indeed I thought a good deal more of the little rascals than I did of the hens; but uncle was dreadfully wrought up and made most disparaging remarks about my woodcraft. To please him I one day took the hound across to the woods and, seating myself on a stump on the open hillside, I bade the dog go on. Within three minutes he sang out in the tongue all hunters know so well, 'Fox! fox! fox! straight away down the valley.'

After a while I heard them coming back. There I saw the

fox—Scarface—loping lightly across the river bottom to the stream. In he went and trotted along in the shallow water near the margin for two hundred yards, then came out straight toward me. Though in full view, he saw me not but came up the hill watching over his shoulder for the hound. Within ten feet of me he turned and sat with his back to me while he craned his neck and showed an eager interest in the doings of the hound. Ranger came bawling along the trail till he came to the running water, the killer of scent, and here he was puzzled; but there was only one thing to do—that was by going up and down both banks find where the fox had left the river.

The fox before me shifted his position a little to get a better view and watched with a most human interest all the circling of the hound. He was so close that I saw the hair of his shoulder bristle a little when the dog came in sight. I could see the jumping of his heart on his ribs, and the gleam of his yellow eye. When the dog was wholly baulked by the water trick it was comical to see—he could not sit still, but rocked up and down in glee and reared on his hind feet to get a better view of the slow-plodding hound. With mouth opened nearly to his ears, though not at all winded, he panted noisily for a moment, or rather he laughed gleefully, just as a dog laughs by grinning and panting.

Old Scarface wriggled in huge enjoyment as the hound puzzled over the trail so long that when he did find it, it was so stale he could barely follow it, and did not feel justified in tonguing on it at all.

As soon as the hound was working up the hill the fox quietly went into the woods. I had been sitting in plain view only ten feet away, but I had the wind and kept still and the fox never knew that his life had for twenty minutes been in the power of the foe he most feared. Ranger also would have passed me as near as the fox, but I spoke to him, and with a little nervous start he quit the trail and, looking sheepish, lay down by my feet.

This little comedy was played with variations for several

days, but it was all in plain view from the house across the river. My uncle, impatient at the daily loss of hens, went out himself, sat on the open knoll, and when old Scarface trotted to his lookout to watch the dull hound on the river flat below my uncle remorselessly shot him in the back, at the very moment when he was grinning over a new triumph.

IV

But still the hens were disappearing. My uncle was wrathy. He determined to conduct the war himself, and sowed the woods with poison baits, trusting to luck that our own dogs would not get them. He indulged in contemptuous remarks on my bygone woodcraft, and went out evenings with a gun and the two dogs, to see what he could destroy.

Vix knew right well what a poisoned bait was; she passed them by or else treated them with active contempt, but one she dropped down the hole of an old enemy, a skunk, who was never afterward seen. Formerly old Scarface was always ready to take charge of the dogs and keep them out of mischief. But now that Vix had the whole burden of the brood she could no longer spend time in breaking every track to the den, and was not always at hand to meet and mislead the foes that might be coming too near.

The end is easily foreseen. Ranger followed a hot trail to the den, and Spot, the fox-terrier, announced that the family was at home, and then did his best to go in after them.

The whole secret was now out, and the whole family doomed. The hired man came around with pick and shovel to dig them out, while we and the dogs stood by. Old Vix soon showed herself in the near woods and led the dogs away off down the river, where she shook them off when she thought proper by the simple device of springing on a sheep's back. The frightened animal ran for several hundred yards, then Vix got off, knowing that there was now a hopeless gap in the scent, and returned to the den. But the dogs, baffled by the break in the trail, soon did the same, to find Vix hanging about in despair, vainly trying to decoy us away from her treasures.

Meanwhile Paddy plied both pick and shovel with vigour and effect. The yellow gravelly sand was heaping on both sides, and the shoulders of the sturdy digger were sinking below the level. After an hour's digging, enlivened by frantic rushes of the dogs after the old fox, who hovered near in the woods, Pat called:

'Here they are, sor!'

It was the den at the end of the burrow, and cowering as far back as they could were the four little woolly cubs.

Before I could interfere a murderous blow from the shovel and a sudden rush for the fierce little terrier ended the lives of three. The fourth and smallest was barely saved by holding him by his tail high out of reach of the excited dogs.

He gave one short squeal, and his poor mother came at the cry, and circled so near that she would have been shot but for the accidental protection of the dogs, who somehow always seemed to get between, and whom she once more led away on a fruitless chase.

The little one saved alive was dropped into a bag, where he lay quite still. His unfortunate brothers were thrown back into their nursery bed, and buried under a few shovelfuls of earth.

We guilty ones then went back into the house, and the little fox

was soon chained in the yard. No one knew just why he was kept alive, but in all a change of feeling had set in, and the idea of killing him was without a supporter.

He was a pretty little fellow, like a cross between a fox and a lamb. His woolly visage and form were strangely lamb-like and innocent, but one could find in his yellow eyes a gleam of cunning and savageness as unlamb-like as it possibly could be.

As long as anyone was near he crouched sullen and cowed in his shelter-box, and it was a full hour after being left alone before he ventured to look out.

My window now took the place of the hollow basswood. A number of hens of the breed he knew so well were about the cub in the yard. Late that afternoon as they strayed near the captive there was a sudden rattle of the chain, and the youngster dashed at the nearest one and would have caught him but for the chain which brought him up with a jerk. He got on his feet and slunk back to his box, and though he afterward made several rushes he so gauged his leap as to win or fail within the length of the chain and never again was brought up by its cruel jerk.

As night came down the little fellow became very uneasy, sneaking out of his box, but going back at each slight alarm, tugging at his chain, or at times biting it in fury while he held it down with his fore-paws. Suddenly he paused as though listening, then raising his little black nose he poured out a short quavering cry.

Once or twice this was repeated, the time between being occupied in worrying the chain and running about. Then an answer came—the far-away '*Yap-yurrr*' of the old fox. A few minutes later a shadowy form appeared on the wood-pile. The little one slunk into his box, but at once returned and ran to meet his mother with all the gladness that a fox could show. Quick as a flash she seized him and turned to bear him away by the road she came. But the moment the end of the chain was reached the cub was rudely jerked from

the old one's mouth and she, scared by the opening of a window, fled over the wood-pile.

An hour afterward the cub had ceased to run about or cry. I peeped out, and by the light of the moon saw the form of the mother at full length on the ground by the little one, gnawing at something—the clank of iron told what—it was that cruel chain. And Tip, the little one, meanwhile was helping himself to a warm drink.

On my going out she fled into the dark woods, but there by the shelter-box were two little mice, bloody and still warm, food for the cub brought by the devoted mother. And in the morning I found the chain was very bright for a foot or two next to the little one's collar.

On walking across the woods to the ruined den I again found signs of Vixen. The poor heartbroken mother had come and dug out the bedraggled bodies of her little ones.

There lay the three little baby foxes all licked smooth now, and by them were two of our hens fresh killed. The newly heaved earth was printed all over with telltale signs—signs that told me that here by the side of her dead she had watched like Rizpah. Here she had brought their usual meal, the spoil of her nightly hunt. Here she had stretched herself beside them and vainly offered them their natural drink and yearned to feed and warm them as of old; but only stiff little bodies under their soft wool she found, and little cold noses still and unresponsive.

A deep impress of elbows, breast and hocks showed where she had lain in silent grief and watched them for long and mourned as a wild mother can mourn for its young. But from that time she came no more to the ruined den, for now she surely knew that her little ones were dead.

V

Tip, the captive, the weakling of the brood, was now the heir to all her love. The dogs were loosed to guard the hens.

The hired man had orders to shoot the old fox on sight—so had I, but was resolved never to see her. Chicken heads, that a fox loves and a dog will not touch, had been poisoned and scattered through the woods; and the only way to the yard where Tip was tied was by climbing the wood-pile after braving all other dangers. And yet each night old Vix was there to nurse her baby and bring it fresh-killed hens and game. Again and again I saw her, although she came now without awaiting the querulous cry of the captive.

The second night of the captivity I heard the rattle of the chain, and then made out that the old fox was there, hard at work digging a hole by the little one's kennel. When it was deep enough to half bury her, she gathered into it all the slack of the chain and filled it again with earth. Then in triumph, thinking she had gotten rid of the chain, she seized little Tip by the neck and turned to dash off up the wood-pile, but alas! only to have him jerked roughly from her grasp.

Poor little fellow, he whimpered sadly as he crawled into his box. After half an hour there was a great outcry among the dogs, and by their straight-away tonguing through the far woods I knew they were chasing Vix. Away up north they went in the direction of the railway, and their noise faded from hearing. Next morning the hounds had not come back. We soon knew why. Foxes long ago learned what a railway is; they soon devised several ways of turning it to account. One way is when hunted to walk the rails for a long distance just before a train comes. The scent, always poor on iron, is destroyed by the train and there is always a chance of hounds being killed by the engine. But another way, more sure but harder to play, is to lead the hounds straight to a high trestle just ahead of the train, so that the engine overtakes them on it and they are surely dashed to destruction.

This trick was skilfully played, and down below we found the mangled remains of old Ranger and learned that Vix was already wreaking her revenge.

That same night she returned to the yard before Spot's weary limbs could bring him back and killed another hen and brought it to Tip, and stretched her panting length beside him that he might quench his thirst. For she seemed to think he had no food but what she brought.

It was that hen that betrayed to my uncle the nightly visits.

My own sympathies were all turning to Vix, and I would have no hand in planning further murders. Next night my uncle himself watched, gun in hand, for an hour. Then when it became cold and the moon clouded over he remembered other important business elsewhere, and left Paddy in his place.

But Paddy was 'onaisy' as the stillness and anxiety of watching worked on his nerves. And the loud *bang! bang!* an hour later left us sure only that powder had been burned.

In the morning we found Vix had not failed her young one. Again next night found my uncle on guard, for another hen had been taken. Soon after dark a single shot was heard, but Vix dropped the game she was bringing and escaped. Another attempt made that night called forth another gun shot. Yet next day it was seen by the brightness of the chain that she had come again and vainly tried for hours to cut that hateful bond.

Such courage and staunch fidelity were bound to win respect, if not toleration. At any rate, there was no gunner in wait next night, when all was still. Could it be of any use? Driven off thrice with gun shots, would she make another try to feed or free her captive young one?

Would she? Hers was a mother's love. There was but one to watch them this time, the fourth night, when the quavering whine of the little one was followed by that shadowy form above the wood-pile.

But carrying no fowl or food that could be seen. Had the keen huntress failed at last? Had she no head of game for this her only charge, or had she learned to trust his captors for his food?

No, far from all this. The wild wood mother's heart and hate were true. Her only thought had been to set him free. All means she knew she tried, and every danger braved to tend him well and help him to be free. But all had failed.

Like a shadow she came and in a moment was gone, and Tip seized on something dropped, and crunched and chewed with relish what she brought. But even as he ate a knife-like pang shot through and a scream of pain escaped him. Then there was a momentary struggle and the little fox was dead.

The mother's love was strong in Vix, but a higher thought was stronger. She knew right well the poison's power; she knew the poison bait, and would have taught him had he lived to know and shun it too. But now at last, when she must choose for him a wretched prisoner's life or sudden death, she quenched the mother in her breast and freed him by the one remaining door.

It is when the snow is on the ground that we take the census of the woods, and when the winter came it told me that Vix no longer roamed the woods of Erindale. Where she went it never told, but only this, that she was gone.

Gone perhaps to some other far-off haunt to leave behind the sad remembrance of her murdered little ones and mate. Or gone maybe, deliberately, from the scene of a sorrowful life, as many a wild wood mother has gone, by the means that she herself had used to free her young one, the last of all her brood.

Wully

The Story of a Yaller Dog

WULLY was a little yaller dog. A yaller dog, be it understood, is not necessarily the same as a yellow dog. He is not simply a canine whose capillary covering is highly charged with yellow pigment. He is the mongrelest mixture of all mongrels, the least common multiple of all dogs, the breedless union of all breeds; and though of no breed at all he is yet of older, better breed than any of his aristocratic relations, for he is nature's attempt to restore the ancestral jackal, the parent stock of all dogs.

Indeed the scientific name of the jackal (*Canis aureus*) means simply 'yellow dog', and not a few of that animal's characteristics are seen in his domesticated representative. For the plebeian cur is shrewd, active and hardy, and far better equipped for the real struggle of life than any of his 'thoroughbred' kinsmen.

If we were to abandon a yaller dog, a greyhound and a bulldog on a desert island, which of them after six months would be alive and well? Unquestionably it would be the despised yellow cur. He has not the speed of the greyhound, but neither does he bear the seeds of lung and skin diseases. He has not the strength or reckless courage of the bulldog, but he has something a thousand times better, he has *common sense*. Health and wit are no mean equipment for the life struggle, and when the dog world is not 'managed' by man, they have never yet failed to bring out the yellow mongrel as the sole and triumphant survivor.

Once in a while the reversion to the jackal type is more complete, and the yaller dog has pricked and pointed ears. Beware of him then. He is cunning and plucky and can bite like a wolf. There is a strange wild streak in his nature, too, that under cruelty or long adversity may develop into deadliest treachery in spite of the better traits that are the foundation of man's love for the dog.

I

Away up in the Cheviots little Wully was born. He and one other of the litter were kept; his brother because he resembled the best dog in the vicinity, and himself because he was a little yellow beauty.

His early life was that of a sheepdog in company with an experienced collie who trained him and an old shepherd who was scarcely inferior to them in intelligence. By the time he was two years old Wully was fully grown and had taken a thorough course in sheep. He knew them from ram-horn to lamb-hoof, and old Robin, his master, at length had such confidence in his sagacity that he would frequently stay at the tavern all night while Wully guarded the woolly idiots in the hills. His education had been wisely bestowed and in most ways he was a very bright little dog with a future before him. Yet he never learned to despise that addle-pated Robin. The old shepherd, with all his faults, his continual striving after his ideal state—intoxication—and his mind-shrivelling life in general, was rarely brutal to Wully, and Wully repaid him with an exaggerated worship that the greatest and wisest in the land would have aspired to in vain.

Wully could not have imagined any greater being than Robin, and yet for the sum of five shillings a week all Robin's vital energy and mental force were pledged to the service of a not very great cattle and sheep dealer, the real proprietor of Wully's charge, and when this man, really less great than the neighbouring laird, ordered Robin to drive his flock by stages to the Yorkshire moors and markets, of all the 376 mentalities concerned, Wully's was the most interested and interesting.

The journey through Northumberland was uneventful. At the River Tyne the sheep were driven on to the ferry and landed safely in smoky South Shields. The great factory chimneys were just starting up for the day and belching out fogbanks and thunder-rollers of opaque leaden smoke that darkened the air and hung low like a storm cloud over the streets. The sheep thought that they recognized the fuming dun of an unusually heavy Cheviot storm. They became alarmed, and in spite of their keepers stampeded through the town in 374 different directions.

Robin was vexed to the inmost recesses of his tiny soul. He stared stupidly after the sheep for half a minute, then gave the order, 'Wully, fetch them in.' After this mental effort he sat down, lit his pipe and, taking out his knitting, began work on a half-finished sock.

To Wully the voice of Robin was the voice of God. Away he ran in 374 different directions, and headed off and rounded up the 374 different wanderers, and brought them back to the ferry-house before Robin, who was stolidly watching the process, had toed off his sock.

Finally Wully—not Robin—gave the sign that all were in. The old shepherd proceeded to count them—370, 371, 372, 373.

'Wully,' he said reproachfully, 'thar no' a' here. Thur's anither.' And Wully, stung with shame, bounded off to scour the whole city for the missing one. He was not long gone when a small boy pointed out to Robin that the sheep were all there, the whole 374. Now Robin was in a quandary. His order was to hasten on to Yorkshire, and yet he knew that Wully's pride would prevent his coming back without another sheep, even if he had to steal it. Such things had happened before and resulted in embarrassing complications. What should he do? There was five shillings a week at stake. Wully was a good dog, it was a pity to lose him, but then, his orders from the master; and again, if Wully stole an extra sheep to make up the number, then what—in a foreign land too? He decided to abandon Wully and push on alone with the sheep. And how he fared no one knows or cares.

Meanwhile Wully careered through miles of streets hunting in vain for his lost sheep. All day he searched, and at night, famished and worn out, he sneaked shamefacedly back to the ferry, only to find that master and sheep had gone. His sorrow was pitiful to see. He ran about whimpering, then took the ferryboat across to the other side, and searched everywhere for Robin. He returned to South Shields and searched there, and spent the rest of the night seeking for his wretched idol. The next day he continued his search, he crossed and recrossed the river many times. He watched and smelt everyone that came over, and with significant shrewdness he sought unceasingly in the neighbouring taverns for his master. The next day he set to work systematically to smell everyone that might cross the ferry.

The ferry makes fifty trips a day, with an average of one hundred persons a trip, yet never once did Wully fail to be on the gang-plank and smell every pair of legs that crossed—five thousand pairs, ten thousand legs that day did Wully examine after his own fashion. And the next day, and the next, and all the week he kept his post, and seemed indifferent to feeding himself. Soon starvation and worry began to tell on him. He grew thin and ill-tempered. No one could touch him, and any attempt to interfere with his daily occupation of leg-smelling roused him to desperation.

Day after day, week after week, Wully watched and waited for his master, who never came. The ferrymen learned to respect Wully's fidelity. At first he scorned their proffered food and shelter, and lived no one knew how, but, starved to it at last, he accepted the gifts and learned to tolerate the givers. Although embittered against the world, his heart was true to his worthless master.

Fourteen months afterward I made his acquaintance. He was still on rigid duty at his post. He had regained his good looks. His bright keen face set off by his white ruff and pricked ears made a dog to catch the eye anywhere. But he gave me no second glance, once he found my legs were not those he sought, and in spite of my friendly overtures during the ten months following that he continued his watch, I got no further into his confidence than any other stranger.

For two whole years did this devoted creature attend that ferry. There was only one thing to prevent him going home to the hills—not the distance, nor the chance of getting lost, but the conviction that Robin, the god-like Robin, wished him to stay by the ferry; and he stayed.

But he crossed the water as often as he felt it would serve his purpose. The fare for a dog was one penny, and it was calculated that Wully owed the company hundreds of pounds before he gave up his quest. He never failed to sense every pair of nethers that crossed the gang-plank—six million legs by computation had been pronounced upon by this expert. But all to no purpose. His unswerving fidelity never faltered, though his temper was obviously souring under the long strain.

We had never heard what became of Robin, but one day a sturdy drover strode down the ferry-slip. Wully mechanically assaying the new personality, suddenly started, his

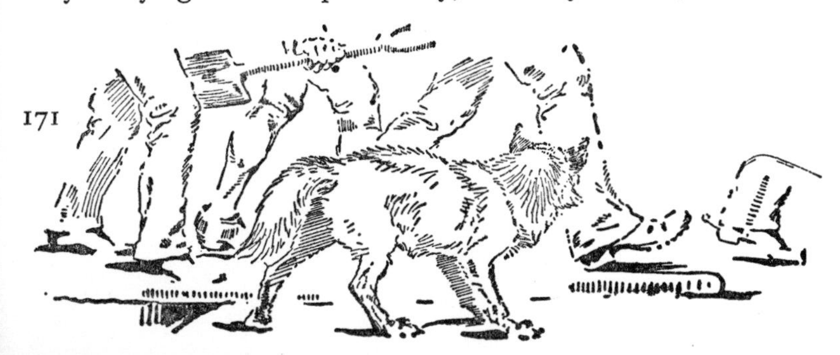

mane bristled, he trembled, a low growl escaped him and he fixed his every sense on the drover.

One of the ferry-hands, not understanding, called to the stranger, 'Hoot, mon, ye maunna hort oor dawg.'

'Whae 's hortin 'im, ye fule; he is mair like to hort me.' But further explanation was not necessary. Wully's manner had wholly changed. He fawned on the drover, and his tail was wagging violently for the first time in years.

A few words made it all clear. Dorley, the drover, had known Robin very well, and the mittens and comforter he wore were of Robin's own make and had once been part of his wardrobe. Wully recognized the traces of his master and, despairing of any nearer approach to his lost idol, he abandoned his post at the ferry and plainly announced his intention of sticking to the owner of the mittens, and Dorley was well pleased to take Wully along to his home among the hills of Derbyshire, where he became once more a sheepdog in charge of a flock.

II

MONSALDALE is one of the best known valleys in Derbyshire. The Pig and Whistle is its single but celebrated inn, and Jo Greatorex, the landlord, is a shrewd and sturdy Yorkshireman. Nature meant him for a frontiersman, but circumstances made him an innkeeper and his inborn tastes made him a—well, never mind; there was a great deal of poaching done in that country.

Wully's new home was on the upland east of the valley above Jo's inn, and that fact was not without weight in bringing me to Monsaldale. His master, Dorley, farmed in a small way on the lowland, and on the moors had a large number of sheep. These Wully guarded with his old-time sagacity, watching them while they fed and bringing them to the fold at night. He was reserved and preoccupied for a dog, and rather too ready to show his teeth to strangers, but he was so unremitting in his attention to his flock that Dorley did not lose a lamb that year, although the neighbouring farmers paid the usual tribute to eagles and to foxes.

The dales are poor fox-hunting country at best. The rocky ridges, high stone walls and precipices are too numerous to please the riders, and the final retreats in the rocks are so plentiful that it was a marvel the foxes did not overrun Monsaldale. But they didn't. There had been but little reason for complaint until the year 1881, when a sly old fox quartered himself on the fat parish like a mouse inside a cheese, and laughed equally at the hounds of the huntsmen and the lurchers of the farmers.

He was several times run by the Peak hounds, and escaped by making for the Devil's Hole. Once in this gorge, where the cracks in the rocks extend unknown distances, he was safe. The country folk began to see something more than chance in the fact that he always escaped at the Devil's Hole, and when one of the hounds who nearly caught this Devil's Fox soon after went mad it removed all doubt as to the spiritual paternity of said fox.

He continued his career of rapine, making audacious raids and hairbreadth escapes, and finally began, as do many old foxes, to kill from a mania for slaughter. Thus it was that Digby lost ten lambs in one night. Carroll lost seven the next night. Later the vicarage duckpond was wholly devastated, and scarcely a night passed but someone in the region had to report a carnage of poultry, lambs or sheep, and finally even calves.

Of course all the slaughter was attributed to this one fox of the Devil's Hole. It was known only that he was a very large fox, at least one that made a very large track. He never was clearly seen, even by the huntsmen. And it was noticed that Thunder and Bell, the staunchest hounds in the pack, had refused to tongue or even to follow the trail when he was hunted.

His reputation for madness sufficed to make the master of

the Peak hounds avoid the neighbourhood. The farmers in Monsaldale, led by Jo, agreed among themselves that if it would only come on to snow they would assemble and beat the whole country and, in defiance of all rules of the hunt, get rid of the 'daft' fox in any way they could. But the snow did not come, and the red-haired gentleman lived his life. Notwithstanding his madness, he did not lack method. He never came two successive nights to the same farm. He never ate where he killed, and he never left a track that betrayed his retreat. He usually finished up his night's trail on the turf or on a public highway.

Once I saw him. I was walking to Monsaldale from Bakewell late one night during a heavy storm, and as I turned the corner of Stead's sheep-fold there was a vivid flash of lightning. By its light there was fixed on my retina a picture that made me start. Sitting on his haunches by the roadside, twenty yards away, was a very large fox gazing at me with malignant eyes and licking his muzzle in a suggestive manner. All this I saw, but no more, and might have forgotten it, or thought myself mistaken, but the next morning, in that very fold, were found the bodies of twenty-three lambs and sheep, and the unmistakable signs that brought home the crime to the well-known marauder.

There was only one man who escaped, and that was Dorley. This was the more remarkable because he lived in the centre of the region raided and within one mile of the Devil's Hole. Faithful Wully proved himself worth all the dogs in the neighbourhood. Night after night he brought in the sheep, and never one was missing. The Mad Fox might prowl about the Dorley homestead if he wished, but Wully, shrewd, brave, active Wully, was more than a match for him, and not only saved his master's flock but himself escaped with a whole skin. Everyone entertained a profound respect for him, and he might have been a popular pet but for his temper which, never genial, became more and more crabbed. He seemed to like Dorley, and Huldah, Dorley's eldest daughter, a shrewd, handsome young woman, who,

in the capacity of general manager of the house, was Wully's special guardian. The other members of Dorley's family Wully learned to tolerate, but the rest of the world, men and dogs, he seemed to hate.

His uncanny disposition was well shown in the last meeting I had with him. I was walking on a pathway across the moor behind Dorley's house. Wully was lying on the doorstep. As I drew near he arose, and without appearing to see me trotted toward my pathway and placed himself across it about ten yards ahead of me. There he stood silently and intently regarding the distant moor, his slightly bristling mane the only sign that he had not been suddenly turned to stone. He did not stir as I came up, and, not wishing to quarrel, I stepped around past his nose and walked on. Wully at once left his position and in the same eerie silence trotted on some twenty feet and again stood across the pathway. Once more I came up and, stepping into the grass, brushed past his nose. Instantly, but without a sound, he seized my left heel. I kicked out with the other foot, but he escaped. Not having a stick I flung a large stone at him. He leaped forward and the stone struck him in the ham, bowling him over into a ditch. He gasped out a savage growl as he fell, but scrambled out of the ditch and limped away in silence.

Yet, sullen and ferocious as Wully was to the world, he was always gentle with Dorley's sheep. Many were the tales of rescues told of him. Many a poor lamb that had fallen into a pond or hole would have perished but for his timely and sagacious aid, many a far-weltered ewe did he turn right side up; while his keen eye discerned and his fierce courage baffled every eagle that had appeared on the moor in his time.

III

THE Monsaldale farmers were still paying their nightly tribute to the Mad Fox, when the snow came, late in December. Poor Widow Gelt lost her entire flock of twenty sheep, and the fiery cross went forth early in the morning. With guns unconcealed the burly farmers set out to follow to the finish the telltale tracks in the snow, those of a very large fox, undoubtedly the multo-murderous villain. For a while the trail was clear enough, then it came to the river and the habitual cunning of the animal was shown. He reached the water at a long angle pointing down stream and jumped into the shallow unfrozen current. But at the other side there was no track leading out, and it was only after long searching that, a quarter of a mile higher up the stream, they found where he had come out. The track then ran to the top of Henley's high stone wall, where there was no snow left to tell tales. But the patient hunters persevered. When it crossed the smooth snow from the wall to the high road there was a difference of opinion. Some claimed that the track went up, others down the road. But Jo settled it, and after another long search they found where apparently the same trail, though some said a larger one, had left the road to enter a sheep-fold, and leaving this without harming the occupants, the track-maker had stepped in the footmarks of a countryman, thereby getting to the moor road, along which he had trotted straight to Dorley's farm.

That day the sheep were kept in on account of the snow, and Wully, without his usual occupation, was lying on some planks in the sun. As the hunters drew near the house he growled savagely and sneaked around to where the sheep were. Jo Greatorex walked up to where Wully had crossed the fresh snow, gave a glance, looked dumbfounded, then pointing to the retreating sheepdog, he said, with emphasis:

'Lads, we're off the track of the fox. But there's the killer of the widder's yowes.'

Some agreed with Jo, other recalled the doubt in the trail and were for going back to make a fresh follow. At this juncture Dorley himself came out of the house.

'Tom,' said Jo, 'that dog o' thine 'as killed twenty of Widder Gelt's sheep, last night. An' ah fur one don't believe as it's 'is first killin'.'

'Why, mon, thou art crazy,' said Tom, 'Ah never 'ad a better sheepdog—'e fair loves the sheep.'

'Aye! We's seen summat o' that in las' night's work,' replied Jo.

In vain the company related the history of the morning. Tom swore that it was nothing but a jealous conspiracy to rob him of Wully.

'Wully sleeps i' the kitchen every night. Never is oot till he's let to bide wi' the yowes. Why, mon, he's wi' oor sheep the year round, and never a hoof have ah lost.'

Tom became much excited over this abominable attempt against Wully's reputation and life. Jo and his partisans got equally angry, and it was a wise suggestion of Huldah's that quieted them.

'Feyther,' said she, 'ah'll sleep i' the kitchen the night. If Wully 'as ae way of gettin' oot ah'll see it, an' if he's no oot an' sheep's killed on the countryside, we'll ha' proof it's na Wully.'

That night Huldah stretched herself on the settee and Wully slept as usual underneath the table. As night wore on the dog became restless. He turned on his bed and once or twice got up, stretched, looked at Huldah and lay down again. About two o'clock he seemed no longer able to resist some strange impulse. He arose quietly, looked toward the low window, then at the motionless girl. Huldah lay still and breathed as though sleeping. Wully slowly came near and sniffed and breathed his doggy breath in her face. She made no move. He nudged her gently with his nose. Then, with his sharp ears forward and his head on one side, he studied her calm face. Still no sign. He walked quietly to the window, mounted the table without noise, placed his nose under the sash-bar and raised the light frame until he could put one paw underneath. Then changing, he put his nose under the sash and raised it high enough to slip out, easing down the frame finally on his rump and tail with an adroitness that told of long practice. Then he disappeared into the darkness.

From her couch Huldah watched in amazement. After waiting for some time to make sure that he was gone, she arose, intending to call her father at once, but on second thought she decided to await more conclusive proof. She peered into the darkness, but no sign of Wully was to be seen. She put more wood on the fire, and lay down again. For over an hour she lay wide awake listening to the kitchen clock, and starting at each trifling sound, and wondering what the dog was doing. Could it be possible that he had really killed the widow's sheep? Then the recollection of his gentleness to their own sheep came, and completed her perplexity.

Another hour slowly tick-tocked. She heard a slight sound at the window that made her heart jump. The scratching sound was soon followed by the lifting of the sash, and in a short time Wully was back in the kitchen with the window closed behind him.

By the flickering firelight Huldah could see a strange wild gleam in his eye, and his jaws and snowy breast were dashed with fresh blood. The dog ceased his slight panting as he scrutinized the girl. Then, as she did not move, he lay down, and began to lick his paws and muzzle, growling lowly once or twice as though at the remembrance of some recent occurrence.

Huldah had seen enough. There could no longer be any doubt that Jo was right and more—a new thought flashed into her quick brain, she realized that the weird fox of Monsal was before her. Raising herself, she looked straight at Wully and exclaimed:

'Wully! Wully! So it's a' true—oh, Wully, ye terrible brute!'

Her voice was fiercely reproachful; it rang in the quiet kitchen, and Wully recoiled as though shot. He gave a desperate glance toward the closed window. His eye gleamed, and his mane bristled. But he cowered under her gaze, and grovelled on the floor as though begging for mercy. Slowly he crawled nearer and nearer, as if to lick her feet, until quite close, then, with the fury of a tiger, but without a sound, he sprang for her throat.

The girl was taken unawares, but she threw up her arm in time, and Wully's long gleaming tusks sank into her flesh and grated on the bone.

'Help! Help! Feyther! Feyther!' she shrieked.

Wully was a light weight, and for a moment she flung him off. But there could be no mistaking his purpose. The game was up—it was his life or hers now.

'Feyther! Feyther!' she screamed, as the yellow fury, striving to kill her, bit and tore the unprotected hands that had so often fed him.

In vain she fought to hold him off; he would soon have had her by the throat, when in rushed Dorley.

Straight at him now in the same horrid silence sprang Wully, and savagely tore him again and again before a deadly blow from the faggot-hook disabled him, dashing him, gasping and writhing, on the stone floor, desperate and done for, but game and defiant to the last. Another quick blow scattered his brains on the hearthstone, where so long he had been a faithful and honoured retainer—and Wully, bright, fierce, trusty, treacherous Wully, quivered a moment, then straightened out and lay for ever still.

FAIRY TALES FROM THE ARABIAN NIGHTS. Illustrated by KIDDELL-MONROE.

Here are the favourite tales—the fairy tales—out of the many told in the 'Thousand and One Nights'.

FAIRY TALES OF LONG AGO. Edited by M. C. CAREY. Illustrated by D. J. WATKINS-PITCHFORD.

This varied collection takes in translations from Charles Perrault, Madame de Beaumont, the Countess d'Aulnoy of France, Asbjörnsen and Moe, etc.

Selma Lagerlöf's THE FURTHER ADVENTURES OF NILS. Illustrated by HANS BAUMHAUER.

Nils's adventures continue with his flight over lake, hill, ice, snow, forest and moor of Sweden. The artist ably interprets the visual contrasts of the journey. (Not available in the U.S.A. in this edition.)

Louisa M. Alcott's GOOD WIVES. Illustrated by S. VAN ABBÉ, R.B.A., A.R.E.

Frances Browne's GRANNY'S WONDERFUL CHAIR. Illustrated by DENYS WATKINS-PITCHFORD.

The author, blind from birth, draws upon the Irish fairy-stories of her childhood to add magic and colour to the whole of this enchanting book.

GRIMMS' FAIRY TALES. Illustrated by CHARLES FOLKARD.

HANS ANDERSEN'S FAIRY TALES. Illustrated by HANS BAUMHAUER.

A new English rendering, including some new and outstanding tales.

Mary Mapes Dodge's HANS BRINKER. Illustrated by HANS BAUMHAUER.

This story is the best known and best loved work of the author.

Johanna Spyri's HEIDI. Illustrated by VINCENT O. COHEN.

This is the famous story of a Swiss child and her life among the Alps.

Charles Kingsley's THE HEROES. Illustrated by KIDDELL-MONROE.

A retelling of the legends of Perseus, the Argonauts and Theseus.

Louisa M. Alcott's JO'S BOYS. Illustrated by HARRY TOOTHILL.

'There is an abiding charm about the story.' *Scotsman.*

A. M. Hadfield's KING ARTHUR AND THE ROUND TABLE. Illustrated by DONALD SETON CAMMELL.

The haunting world of the Round Table.

Charlotte M. Yonge's THE LITTLE DUKE. Illustrated by MICHAEL GODFREY.

The story of Richard the Fearless, Duke of Normandy from 942 to 996.

Frances Hodgson Burnett's LITTLE LORD FAUNTLEROY

'The best version of the Cinderella story in a modern idiom that exists.

MARGHANITA LASKI.

Louisa M. Alcott's LITTLE MEN. Illustrated by HARRY TOOTHILL.

Harry Toothill's drawings capture the liveliness of a young gentlemen's academy.

Louisa M. Alcott's LITTLE WOMEN. Illustrated by S. VAN ABBÉ.

S. van Abbé's drawings capture the vivacity and charm of the March family.

Mrs Ewing's LOB LIE-BY-THE-FIRE and THE STORY OF A SHORT LIFE. Illustrated by RANDOLPH CALDECOTT ('Lob') and H. M. BROCK ('Short Life').

Two of Mrs Ewing's most charming stories.

MODERN FAIRY STORIES. Edited by ROGER LANCELYN GREEN. Illustrated by E. H. SHEPARD.

Original (not 'retold') fairy stories by thirteen authors of modern times.

Jean Ingelow's MOPSA THE FAIRY. Illustrated by DORA CURTIS.
A river journey leads to the realms of wonder.

NURSERY RHYMES. Collected and illustrated in two-colour line by A. H. WATSON.
A comprehensive book of nursery rhymes.

Carlo Collodi's PINOCCHIO. The Story of a Puppet. Illustrated by CHARLES FOLKARD.
The most enchanting story of a puppet ever written.

Andrew Lang's PRINCE PRIGIO and PRINCE RICARDO. Illustrated by D. J. WATKINS-PITCHFORD.
Two modern fairy-tales, rich in romantic adventures.

George MacDonald's THE LOST PRINCESS
THE PRINCESS AND CURDIE
THE PRINCESS AND THE GOBLIN
The first two volumes illustrated by CHARLES FOLKARD, the third by D. J. WATKINS-PITCHFORD.

Carola Oman's ROBIN HOOD. Illustrated by S. VAN ABBÉ.
Carola Oman lends substance to the 'Prince of Outlaws'

W. M. Thackeray's THE ROSE AND THE RING and Charles Dickens's THE MAGIC FISH-BONE.
Two children's stories, the first containing the author's illustrations, the latter containing PAUL HOGARTH'S work.

John Hampden's SIR WILLIAM AND THE WOLF, etc. Illustrated by ERIC FRASER.
'Assuredly another treasure chest.' *Scotsman.*

J. R. Wyss's THE SWISS FAMILY ROBINSON. Illustrated by CHARLES FOLKARD.
This is a new version by Audrey Clark of the popular classic.

Charles and Mary Lamb's TALES FROM SHAKESPEARE. Illustrated by ARTHUR RACKHAM.

TALES OF MAKE-BELIEVE. Edited by ROGER LANCELYN GREEN. Illustrated by HARRY TOOTHILL.
Charles Dickens, Rudyard Kipling, E. Nesbit, Thomas Hardy, E. V. Lucas, etc.

Nathaniel Hawthorne's TANGLEWOOD TALES. Illustrated by S. VAN ABBÉ.
This is a sequel to the famous *Wonder Book.*

Thomas Hughes's TOM BROWN'S SCHOOLDAYS. Illustrated by S. VAN ABBÉ.
'The best story of a boy's schooldays ever written.'

Charles Kingsley's THE WATER-BABIES. Illustrated by ROSALIE K. FRY.
The artist's drawings delicately interpret the fantastic beauty of the underwater world.

Nathaniel Hawthorne's A WONDER BOOK. Illustrated by S. VAN ABBÉ.
Hawthorne's famous *Wonder Book* recalls the immortal fables of antiquity.

Selma Lagerlöf's THE WONDERFUL ADVENTURES OF NILS. Illustrated by HANS BAUMHAUER.
Translated into most languages of the world, this Swedish tale of the boy who rode on the back of a young gander and flew northwards to find surprising adventures is a great favourite. (Not available in the U.S.A. in this edition.)

Illustrated Classics for Older Readers

Robert Louis Stevenson's THE BLACK ARROW. Illustrated by LIONEL EDWARDS.
The period is the England of the Wars of the Roses.

Charles Dickens's A CHRISTMAS CAROL and THE CRICKET ON THE HEARTH.
Illustrated by C. E. BROCK.

Cervantes's DON QUIXOTE. Illustrated by W. HEATH ROBINSON.
An edition suitably edited from the Cervantes original.

Jonathan Swift's GULLIVER'S TRAVELS. Illustrated by ARTHUR RACKHAM.
Gulliver's Travels is one of the great satires in the English language.

Robert Louis Stevenson's KIDNAPPED. Illustrated by G. OAKLEY.
A great adventure story and companion piece to *Treasure Island.*

H. Rider Haggard's KING SOLOMON'S MINES. Illustrated by A. R. WHITEAR.
A witch and treasure hunt in the heart of Africa.

R. D. Blackmore's LORNA DOONE. Illustrated by LIONEL EDWARDS.
An edition capturing the spirit of this evergreen romance.

John Bunyan's THE PILGRIM'S PROGRESS. Illustrated by FRANK C. PAPÉ.
The volume contains the first and second parts of the famous 'progress'.

Anthony Hope's THE PRISONER OF ZENDA. Illustrated by MICHAEL GODFREY.
The great Ruritanian romance.

Daniel Defoe's ROBINSON CRUSOE. Illustrated by J. AYTON-SYMINGTON.
An illustrated version which matches Defoe's great adventure story.

Anthony Hope's RUPERT OF HENTZAU. Illustrated by MICHAEL GODFREY.
The enthralling sequel to *The Prisoner of Zenda,* and telling how Rudolf Rassendyll once again in company with Fritz and Sapt saved the honour of the Elphbergs.

H. W. Longfellow's SONG OF HIAWATHA. Illustrated by KIDDELL-MONROE.
The romantic beauty of the legends imaginatively depicted.

John Buchan's THE THIRTY-NINE STEPS. Illustrated by EDWARD ARDIZZONE.
One of the most exciting of Secret Service novels.

Mark Twain's TOM SAWYER
HUCKLEBERRY FINN
These two Twain classics are superbly illustrated by C. WALTER HODGES.

Ernest Thompson Seton's THE TRAIL OF THE SANDHILL STAG and Other Lives of the Hunted. Illustrated with drawings by the author and coloured frontispiece by RITA PARSONS.

Robert Louis Stevenson's TREASURE ISLAND. Illustrated by S. VAN ABBÉ.
Probably no other illustrator of this famous tale has portrayed so vividly the characters in a book that lives so long in a boy's imagination.

Frank L. Baum's THE WONDERFUL WIZARD OF OZ. Illustrated by B. S. BIRO.

Further volumes in preparation